Mills & Boon
Best Seller Romance

A chance to read and collect some of the best-loved novels
from Mills & Boon—the world's largest publisher of romantic fiction.

Every month, four titles by favourite Mills & Boon authors
will be re-published in the *Best Seller Romance* series.

A list of other titles in the *Best Seller Romance* series can be
found at the end of this book.

Roberta Leigh

TEMPORARY WIFE

MILLS & BOON LIMITED
LONDON · TORONTO

First published 1975
Australian copyright 1981
Philippine copyright 1981
This edition 1981

© Roberta Leigh 1975

ISBN 0 263 73507 9

Set in 10 on 11 pt. Linotype Plantin

*Made and printed in Great Britain by
Richard Clay (The Chaucer Press) Ltd, Bungay, Suffolk*

CHAPTER ONE

LUKE ADAMS flung his pen on the desk and swivelled round in his chair to stare moodily through the window. From his sumptuously furnished office on the twenty-first floor he had a superb view of the City of London. He was not aware of it, however, for he was more concerned with what was happening to his own life than the life of the city set out below him. Managing Director of Harrick Investment Trust. It was no mean achievement to be offered this position after only two years with the company, and an even greater achievement when one considered that his background prior to this had been an academic one. But he was still not sure whether to accept the job. His dark brows, thick and well curved, met above his long straight nose as he frowned and turned back to face the desk.

A year ago he would never have believed he would have any doubts about accepting this plum position if it were offered to him. Yet now he was as hesitant and nervous as a virgin. And all because of Gina—Charles Harrick's wife. As always the thought of her filled him with desire and, as always, the desire filled him with repugnance for his weakness in allowing a woman to place him in such an invidious position. For what could be more invidious than to be in love with the wife of the man you worked for, the man whose job you were being groomed to take over?

The door opened and his secretary came in: an efficient, middle-aged woman whom he had inherited with this magnificent office.

'It's all right, Mrs. Benson,' he said as he saw her hesitate. 'I've signed all the letters for the post.'

She came across to the desk and picked up the folder. 'Will you be needing me any more, Mr. Adams?'

'No, thanks.' Aware that she was wondering why he should be sitting here, with his desk clear and no papers to hand, he said with a slight smile: 'I'm summoning up my strength for the next battle.'

'I'd have thought you would be content to enjoy the victory of your last one.'

'When it is the last, it's in the past; and my concern is with the future.'

'Don't you ever get tired of business, Mr. Adams?'

'I love it.'

She smiled and, murmuring goodnight, went out.

Alone again he reached for a cigar, slowly rolling it between his fingers. How different his life was today from what it had been two years ago. He would be the first to concede that it was due to luck as much as ability, for without one the other could often be meaningless. But it looked as though his luck had failed him now. His frown this time was deeper, and anyone watching him would have been surprised by it, for he was frequently referred to in the press as poker-faced. It was a description he played up for all it was worth, knowing that the less he gave away of himself the stronger his position would be. How few people knew the man behind the mask. He was even beginning to feel he no longer knew himself. Flinging down his cigar, he swung round to the window once more. It was dark and wintry and the lights of the rush hour traffic covered the road below in a sprawling gleam of light that moved forward inch by inch. In the dark pane of glass his head and shoulders were reflected, his hair so light blond that it appeared silver, his skin so pale that it looked colourless until one noticed the faint flush on the wide cheekbones, the bluish tinge to the eyelids, the pink of the wide, tightly controlled mouth.

He stretched his arms and yawned, his powerful shoulders straining at the impeccably cut suit. Then he ran his hands through his hair, disarraying its thick strands before he pushed back his chair and got to his feet. Standing, he looked even bigger, his massive frame dominating the desk. But he walked with unexpected grace: quietly, like a panther, giving the impression of a man whose energies

6

were held tightly in check, always ready to pounce. Only his voice, when he spoke, would serve to detract from this picture of controlled energy, for it was deceptively soft and gentle, the words measured and slow as though each one was weighed carefully before being said. But the look in the watchful grey eyes was sharp, warning the perceptive on-looker of the agile mind behind the broad, unlined fore-head.

He put the cigar in his mouth and lit it. There was no let-up in the traffic and he decided to wait a while before leav-ing the office. He thought of telephoning the doorman to let his chauffeur know he would be delayed, and then decided against it. It was part of a chauffeur's job to wait, and though he himself would have found the tedium unendur-able, he must remember that not all men thought as he did. Charles Harrick, for example, never considered other people. It was part of his strength that he cared for the select few whom he believed to be necessary to the success of his company and his own personal happiness. Lucky I'm one of the select band, Luke Adams mused, and rubbed a blunt-ended finger across his cheek. The skin rasped slightly even though his fairness hid a five o'clock shadow. As always the thought of Charles led him to Charles's wife: too young to be tied to a man of sixty, she yet car-ried off her position with aplomb, the way she carried off everything; the way she had carried him into a situation that was now threatening to wreck his career.

Roger's visit to him this afternoon had come as a shock, and the content of his conversation even more so. But he had to decide what to do about it, even though he had still not found a solution. No, that was not true. He knew ex-actly what the solution was, the only reason he was hesitat-ing was because he knew that to do it would destroy every-thing he had worked for these past two years. Two years. He glanced round the room, enjoying, as he always did, the uncluttered lines of the Swedish furniture, the thick carpet and drapes, the few select but highly expensive pictures on

7

the wall. Gina's taste, of course, for she had designed it for him as a present from herself and Charles. But she had put her love into it, a love which he had believed only he knew about: until he had discovered today that Roger knew too. Heaven knew how, but he did.

There was a light tap at the door and he tilted his head as it opened. A woman stood there, the dark wood lintel making a perfect foil for her tall, slim figure with its proud head marked by shining red-gold hair. As always when he saw Gina he was struck by her exquisite beauty, by the way every part of her blended into one graceful whole: the delicate features, the full soft mouth and large blue eyes; the fluid way she walked, moving from the hips the way American women did, although there was no one more English than Gina. It wasn't just her walk that was American either; she had the same elegant grooming.

'Share the joke with me,' she said softly, closing the door and coming further into the room.

'I was thinking how perfect you look.'

'What a lovely compliment to receive on a foggy November afternoon.'

She came closer still, but did not kiss him. They had always been careful when they met in the Harrick building, determined never to give anyone a chance to gossip. Yet Roger had found out. Again Luke wondered how. Either he or Gina had been careless; and if Roger knew, did anyone else?

'I've come to congratulate you,' Gina sat down and crossed one ankle behind the other.

It was a studied gesture, the way most of her gestures were, but Luke drew satisfaction from the slender feet shod in hand-made suede shoes. Not a penny less than fifty pounds, those shoes. He pushed the thought aside, irritated for thinking it. What did money matter to him when he could now afford not to count it? But would that last? What would happen to him if Roger carried out his threat and told Charles that the man whom he had asked to be his Managing Director was also in love with his wife?

'We've slipped up somehow,' he said aloud. 'Our secret's out.'

Gina stared at him. 'You don't mean Charles?'

'Not yet.' Because he longed to take her in his arms, Luke put his desk between them. 'Roger,' he said.

The blue eyes widened. 'But how? We've always been so careful. No one knows—I swear it.'

'I'd have sworn it too, until three o'clock this afternoon. That's when he came to see me. I thought it was to congratulate me on my new position, but it was to issue an ultimatum.'

'What do you mean?'

'Your nephew by marriage has given me a choice,' Luke said heavily. 'Either I give you up or he will tell his uncle about us.'

'He'd never do that! He knows very well the shock would kill him. It's the reason *we* haven't told Charles.' She jumped up and came to stand beside him. Her body trembled with agitation and it was an effort to stop himself from pulling her into his arms. But he knew he must not touch her or kiss her unless they were absolutely certain they were alone. It had been a caution that had stood them in good stead ... until now, when it seemed that all their care had been seen through.

'How did he find out?' Gina asked.

'I'm not sure. What he did say was that he was the only one who knew, and he would be prepared to keep quiet about it if I either stopped seeing you or ...' Luke picked up a pencil and twirled it between his hands; large hands but beautifully shaped, with well-cared-for nails and strong thumbs.

'Or what?' Gina pressed.

'Or turn down Charles's offer of becoming Managing Director.'

'You can't turn it down! You're the only one capable of doing the job. It's what you've been working for.'

'Then are you suggesting I give *you* up?' He tried to make his words light, but he knew his voice was heavy. He

9

loved Gina more than he had ever loved any woman. It was unthinkable to give her up. If only Charles didn't have a bad heart. If it hadn't been for that, he and Gina would never have had to live such a lie. He could have persuaded her to come away with him a year ago. But always the thought of what the shock of it would do to Charles had prevented them from taking the final step. Even now he knew that given the chance, he would rather have Gina than this plum job that had been offered to him. He had sufficient belief in his ability to know he could always find another ladder to climb. But he could not find another Gina. It had taken him thirty-three years to find this one.

'We'll have to tell Roger we'll stop seeing each other.' Gina resumed her chair on the other side of the desk and reached into her handbag for a cigarette. 'It might be as well if I talked to him too.' The beautifully arched red-gold brows, several shades darker than the wavy hair, met in a frown. 'Are you absolutely sure he knows about us—that it wasn't an inspired guess?'

'There was no guesswork in what he said to me.' Luke flung the pencil away from him. 'He knew we were together the weekend Charles went into the Clinic for a check-up, and he knows we meet on a Thursday afternoon.'

'It's Colette.' Gina's beautiful blue eyes darkened. 'He must have got it from her.'

'If you *will* have a French maid who looks as if she should be playing the lead in a French farce...' Luke said with an attempt at lightheartedness.

'I'll fire her at once!' Gina burst out, 'and I'll make sure she never gets a job as a lady's maid again. One thing you expect from people like that is trustworthiness. It's like having your tailor rat on you.'

Against his will, Luke laughed, amused by the fact that even the most clever woman could show a cheerful naïvety when it came to her personal well-being. 'I will have to find another job too,' he said quietly, and then added: 'I don't suppose you would care to get divorced from Charles and marry me?'

'You know I can't.' She leaned forward and the perfume that he always associated with her wafted into his nostrils. 'If Charles wasn't a sick man I'd have left him a year ago—when we knew we loved each other.'

'Would you? Sometimes I think you set too much store by your position.'

'How can you say that!' Forgetting that they were normally careful when they were in the Harrick building, she came round the desk and twined her arms round him. 'I love you, Luke. If I didn't, I would never have put myself in this position. Do you think I enjoy all this secrecy? The pretence and the lies we have to tell? Oh, darling, I'm so afraid when you speak like this.'

'Afraid of what?'

'That you don't want me any more.'

'Don't want you!' His voice was ragged. 'I want you so much I can't think straight! You're like a disease in my blood.'

'Sometimes I think you hate me because of it.'

'Never!' he said vehemently. 'I love you. I love you.' He pulled her close, but when he went to kiss her she turned her head away. 'What's it to be, Gina?' he asked, forcing his mind away from her nearness and back to the original problem. 'If you won't tell Charles—and I can understand why—then I have no choice but to resign and look for another position.'

Immediately she looked at him, her eyes glittering with tears. 'You can't do that. I won't let you destroy your career because of me. *I'll* talk to Roger.'

'You won't get him to change his mind. I had a go at him this afternoon, but he was adamant.'

'Have you thought what Charles will say when you tell him you don't want to be Managing Director?'

'I hadn't thought as far as that,' Luke admitted.

'Then it's time you did.' Gina pulled herself from his hold and went back to her chair, mistress of the situation again. 'And it's time that Roger did too. Ask him to come and see us.'

'Now?' Luke was surprised.

'Why not? The longer you allow a bad situation to go on, the worse it will get. Roger's made a threat and we have to meet it.'

'Are you suggesting we stop seeing each other?'

'As far as Roger is concerned, yes. We wouldn't, of course, but—'

'It won't work. If he could find out about us, he'd soon find out we were trying to fool him.'

'Not if I got rid of Colette. I'm sure he paid her to spy on me. He's always hated me for marrying his uncle.'

'That's understandable. He was frightened you would have children and deplete his inheritance.'

Tears overflowed from Gina's eyes and Luke cursed himself for having spoken. 'I'm sorry, darling, I know how badly you feel about not having children.'

'I don't think you do,' she whispered. 'If I had known Charles couldn't have any, I would never have married him.'

'It was a crazy thing to do, anyway,' Luke said hoarsely. 'He's old enough to be your father.'

'Try and understand,' she pleaded. 'He was charming and sophisticated and I was young and just out of finishing school. He showered me with flowers, clothes, jewels . . . all the things a silly girl dreams of.'

'Weren't there younger men willing to do the same?'

'None of them had Charles's charm,' Gina sighed heavily. 'And of course my father knew him in the City, and you know what a world of its own the City is, with Charles one of its ruling princes. I suppose *that* turned my head more than anything else.'

It was a story Luke had heard before and, as always, he thought what a waste it was that this lovely, vital woman should have tied herself to a man thirty years her senior. Her parents must have been crazy to have let her do it, though gossip had it that they had used their daughter's beauty as a financial asset. Yet even marriage to Charles

Harrick could have been broken had it not been for his ill health.

'Charles isn't getting any better,' Gina murmured, as if aware of the path his thoughts had taken. 'He went for a check-up the other day and I spoke to Sir Daniel James afterwards. He said it's just a question of time.'

'If he takes things easy, he can go on for years,' Luke replied.

'He won't go on for years. You know that as well as I do. That's why we must play for time.'

'And how do we keep Roger quiet meanwhile?'

'I don't know.' She looked at the telephone and gave a wry smile. 'It will seem strange to admit to another person that you and I are in love. Do you know, Roger will be the first person I've ever said it to?'

'I would like to shout it from the rooftops,' Luke said, and then gave an embarrassed laugh. 'You make me talk like a schoolboy.'

'You don't act like one,' she said huskily, and held out her hand to him. 'Are you free this weekend, darling? Charles is going into the Clinic again.'

'I'm always free,' Luke reminded her. '*You* are the one who finds it difficult!'

Ignoring this, Gina pointed to the telephone again and he picked it up and asked the switchboard to connect him with Roger Harrick.

'I would like to see you in my office at once,' he said when the younger man came on the line, and replaced the telephone without waiting for a reply. 'Well,' he said to Gina, 'have you worked out what you're going to say to him?'

'Not yet. But don't worry, darling, I'm a good musician and I'll play it by ear.'

Coming into Luke's office, Roger's pale face grew paler as he saw Gina sitting there. 'Hello, Gina,' he said stiltedly.

'Hello, Roger,' Gina said in her gentlest tone. 'Luke has just told me that you know we love each other.'

Roger looked nonplussed, as if he had not expected such

a frank admission of their affection.

'There's no point in the three of us pretending,' Gina continued. 'Now that you know the truth about Luke and myself, you're part of the secret. A cosy triangle, you might say.' There was a pause. 'Unless you've told anyone else?'

'No one,' Roger replied. 'It isn't something I would care to talk about.'

'I don't care to talk about it either, but you've made it impossible for me not to do so.'

'I don't want to cause you any trouble, Gina,' Roger said quickly. 'I'm only concerned with Uncle Charles.'

'Do you think I'm not concerned with Charles too? Why else do you think I've stayed with him these past five years?'

'You're his wife; why shouldn't you stay with him?'

'Because he isn't my husband any longer. He hasn't been since the year after we were married!'

Colour stained Roger's cheeks, making him look younger than his twenty-six years. 'I'm sorry. I had no idea.'

'Why should you have? It isn't something one broadcasts.'

'Please don't say any more. Your private life is——'

'*Your* concern,' Gina interrupted. 'You've made my affairs your business, so the least you can do is to hear the whole story. Your uncle has been ill a long time and it affected our physical life together long before his illness became publicly known. If I'd been tougher I would have left him then. He offered to divorce me, you know, but because I loved him as a person I couldn't bring myself to hurt him. So I stayed and tried to make myself believe that I could live without love: without having the happiness that . . .' She paused and glanced at the man behind the desk. 'And I did until I met Luke.'

'Do you think it necessary to acquaint Roger with your feelings?' Luke's voice was hard.

'I'm trying to make him understand why I fell in love with you; that it wasn't because I had stopped loving

14

Charles.' She looked at Roger again. 'My feelings for your uncle remain unchanged. I never wanted to hurt him, and I still don't.'

'Neither do I,' Roger said.

'But you're threatening to tell him about Luke and myself. And that will hurt him very much indeed.'

Roger shook his head. 'He's bound to find out sooner or later.'

'He hasn't done so far.'

'Because up till now you've been careful. But in the last few months you haven't. That's how *I* found out.'

'How *did* you?' Gina asked.

'I had to deliver some documents to Luke's flat one evening. Instead of leaving them with a porter I went to talk to him. I wanted to ask his advice about a transaction I was dealing with. I heard your voice behind the door.' He paused uncomfortably and then braced his shoulders. 'You were calling something to Luke and it was pretty obvious that you were more than just friends.'

Luke cast his mind back to the one and only time—a month ago—when Gina had come to his flat. Always until then they had chosen their meeting places with discretion, but the week before he had been out of town and on his return to London their need to see each other had been so great that it had overcome their normal care. Fury engulfed him and he longed to get up and catch Roger by the throat; but he swallowed hard and forced himself to remain passive: a display of violence at this stage would do more harm than good.

'But why destroy Luke's career?' Gina was saying. 'I am as much to blame as he is.'

'I don't agree.'

Roger flung Luke a look of anger and he returned it implacably. It was as he thought. The man was jealous of him; jealous of his success with women and in particular his success with Gina. Perhaps the fellow even loved her himself and had entertained hopes of marrying her when his uncle died. It was an interesting thought and he wondered

15

what Roger would say if he mentioned it. For the moment he decided to hold his peace and keep that card up his sleeve.

'If Luke turns down Charles's offer, he'll have to give him a good reason,' Gina said.

'I'm sure he can think of one.'

'He will also be able to find another position with one of our rivals,' she added.

'So what?'

'So how do you think your uncle will react to that? Charles has been grooming Luke to become Managing Director. He has told him all the plans he has for the company; secret plans which no one except Luke and Charles know about. And what sort of loyalty do you expect Luke to have towards Harrick Investments if you force him to leave?'

Roger flung out his hands. During Gina's speech he had been growing more and more agitated and he was not sufficiently master of himself to hide it.

'You hadn't thought of that, had you?' Gina pursued him relentlessly. 'You just thought you could go to a man like Luke and blackmail him into doing what you wanted.'

'I am doing it to protect my uncle.'

'By getting rid of the one person who can take the responsibility off his shoulders?' Gina's voice was clear as a bell as she defied Roger to tell her that what she had said was untrue.

But he ignored the question and answered it with another. 'Don't you think my uncle can find someone else? Luke isn't irreplaceable.'

'Your uncle wouldn't agree with you. He searched for three years before he found Luke, and it's taken him two more years to groom him for the position. Do you honestly think he can find someone else?'

'In time he will.'

'Time is the one thing Charles hasn't got! For heaven's sake, Roger, be logical about it.'

'I'm trying to be,' he burst out, 'but all I can think of is you and Luke making a fool of my uncle! How do you think he would feel if he found out for himself?'

'He won't find out unless you tell him.'

'Sooner or later someone else is bound to know,' Roger said with a shake of his head. 'That's why you have to stop now.'

'And if we refuse?' Luke intervened.

'I'll tell my uncle the truth.'

'Then I have no choice but to leave the company. For I have no intention of giving up Gina.'

'You can't leave,' Gina cried. 'What will you tell Charles?' She glared at Roger. 'Charles regards Luke as a member of his family. If Luke goes, he'll think he's reneging on his promise.'

Roger lowered his head and hunched his shoulders forward. 'There is only one way that would make it possible for Luke to stay here. You would both have to promise to end your affair.'

Luke opened his mouth to speak, but saw a warning gleam in Gina's eyes. Not knowing what she was trying to convey, he remained silent. If his time in the City had taught him nothing else, it had taught him the value of the North country maxim: when in doubt, say nowt.

'If Luke and I give you that promise,' Gina murmured, 'does that mean you would say nothing to Charles?'

Roger ran the tip of his tongue across his lower lip. 'I would want more than a promise.'

'What do you mean?'

'I wouldn't just take your word for it.' Roger glanced at Luke. 'I'd need proof.'

With an effort Luke controlled his temper, though the urge to smash his fist into Roger's baby face was becoming overwhelming.

But his voice was, as always, mild. 'And how am I supposed to give you proof that I have—that I'm not seeing Gina?'

'By marrying someone else.' Roger looked from Luke to Gina, his triumphant expression saying that at least he knew he had succeeded in taking hold of the scene. 'Well,'

17

he muttered, 'will you?'

Luke stared into Gina's eyes, but though they burned with blue intensity, he could not read any meaning in them, and he swung round on the man. 'I'm damned if I'll let you dictate to me! Your uncle is a sick man. At the most, he has a couple of years to live. You're crazy if you think I'll tie myself to another woman. As soon as Gina is free we'll get married. I'd marry her tomorrow if she'd say the word.'

'I'm not interested in your future with Gina,' Roger said bluntly. 'My only concern is for my uncle's happiness, and as of this moment you are the one who is threatening it. If you don't want to resign and get out of Gina's life, then the——'

'Give us time to think about it,' Gina interrupted him.

'How much time?' Roger asked. 'Uncle Charles is making a statement about Luke to the press tomorrow afternoon. If Luke is going to turn down the offer...'

'We'll decide what to do before tomorrow afternoon. The quicker you leave us alone, the quicker we'll be able to reach a decision.'

Roger went to the door. 'Please don't think I want to hurt you, either of you. But Uncle Charles brought me up and—and he's like a father to me.'

'For heaven's sake stop playing Hamlet!' Luke growled. 'Get out and leave us alone.'

CHAPTER TWO

GINA disliked being in a situation over which she had no control. Yet here she was, faced with the most dramatic decision of her life with little chance of manoeuvring it, the way she normally manoeuvred everything that was important to her. And all because Roger had delivered some ridiculous documents to Luke's flat a couple of months ago.

She wanted to jump up and scream; to fling her arms in the air and shout that no one was going to tell her what to do with her life. But the habit of years kept her calmly in her chair, hands in her lap, looking for all the world as if she did not have a single worry when she was, in fact, facing the most traumatic moment she could remember. She dared not let Luke go to another company. Not because she was afraid he might give Harrick secrets away—which she had allowed Roger to believe—but because she feared that if he worked in a different milieu he would form a social life in which she would play no significant role. More important still, once he no longer worked for Charles he would no longer have the same loyalty towards him, and would eventually give her an ultimatum: either she left Charles or he would end their love affair.

The first and only time Luke had said this she had managed to talk him out of it, but it had not been easy, and she had had to play on Charles's heart condition and his need of Luke to run the company before she had won her argument. Luke's appointment as the new Managing Director had made her feel that at last she could breathe more easily, for the very importance of his position would act as a brake on him, making him realise that to run away with the wife of his Chairman, and probably cause the Chairman's untimely death, would do his reputation no good whatever.

But now Roger was threatening to destroy everything she had planned; not just the present satisfactory position of her life—a multi-millionaire husband and a virile adoring lover—but her future too. Luke was not an easy man to fool and it required constant vigilance to maintain his illusion of her. Sometimes she wondered what he would say if he knew that far from staying with Charles because she cared about his health, she was staying because she had given him her youth and intended to remain with him until he died and she became possessor of his fortune. How horrified Luke would be if he knew how mercenary she was, and how little sympathy he would have for her reasons for it. Never knowing the shame of having to pretend to a position one could not afford—which her parents had done throughout her childhood—he had no conception of her obsessive need for financial security.

Yet much as she wanted Charles's money she had no intention of giving up Luke. More than any man she had known, and she had loved many, though Luke had no idea of this, she wanted him more than anyone else in her life. From the moment Charles had brought him to dinner and asked him to join Harricks, she had seen herself as his wife. With Charles's health failing she had thought it only a matter of time before she and Luke could openly declare their love, and things would have worked out as she had planned had it not been for Roger. Fury made her tremble. How she longed to get her hands on him and throttle him!

'Darling, don't be upset,' Luke interrupted her thoughts, and she saw he was bending protectively over her. 'I can't bear to see you trembling,' he continued, and regardless that they were in his office, pulled her into his arms.

She rested against him, her mind racing as she tried to project herself into the future. Luke must not be allowed to go. Yet Roger said he would only let him stay if he were married. The thought aroused another wave of anger and she trembled again.

'Darling,' Luke begged, 'there's no point getting upset. It isn't the end of the world. Mark Watson will be more than glad to take me; and they aren't Harrick rivals either.'

'I won't let you work for anyone else. This company is

your future—*our* future.'

'We won't have a future if I stay on here,' he said grimly. 'Roger isn't bluffing, Gina. He *will* tell Charles. We can't go on pretending any longer.'

'We *could* if you were married to someone else.'

Luke drew back a step to look into her eyes. 'Do you know what you're saying?'

She hesitated. The words had come out of their own volition and she wondered what had prompted them; it was obviously something in the back of her mind, though she could not bring it into consciousness. When Roger had first told them the only way in which he would allow Luke to remain as Managing Director, she had dismissed the idea at once. But now she was beginning to see some merit in the suggestion. If she could marry Luke to some nondescript girl who would remain his wife until she herself were free to marry him, she would be achieving two objectives: enable Luke to stay here and, by tying him to a marriage of convenience, ensure he was not free for anyone else. But where to find a girl willing to be a temporary wife? It was not a post that one could advertise, and the tact and secrecy it required necessitated finding a girl with loyalty, integrity and a pressing need for money.

Emily Lamb. The name, and an image of the girl, flashed into her mind. Of course, the very person for the job.

'Marriage for you might be the best way out,' she said slowly. 'Not a real marriage, of course, but a contractual arrangement.' She was delighted at her choice of words, for they brought the discussion on to a business level instead of an emotional one, and Luke straightened and rested his weight against the side of his desk.

'It would solve all our problems,' she continued, 'if you were to marry some quiet, well-spoken girl. You could continue with your work here—and I'm sure you don't want to give it up after all the effort you've put in—and you could go on seeing me.'

'I can go on seeing you if I work for Mark Watson.'

'Charles would be far more likely to be suspicious then.'

'So what?' Luke said. 'We wouldn't need to be secretive if I weren't working here.'

'We aren't keeping our love secret because you work here, but because we don't want to hurt Charles. My leaving him would kill him. You know that as well as I do.'

Luke wished he could deny it, but honesty would not let him. Charles adored Gina, and to take her away from him could well be a shock from which he could not recover. 'Then we'll have to keep our affair a secret until . . .' He stopped, unable to say the words 'until Charles dies', even though he knew they were implied. 'But I can't go on working here—and at least my leaving will ensure Roger keeps quiet, which is what we both want.'

'How do you think Charles will react to your going?' Gina cried. 'You can't throw his job back in his face and walk out. It would destroy him.'

'Charles isn't so easily destroyed by business setbacks.'

'He wouldn't regard your going as a business setback but as a personal one. I wasn't lying when I told Roger that Charles looks upon you as his son.'

Once again Luke could not deny what Gina had said. Yet neither could he consider marrying anyone else. He thought of the few women he had taken out in the past year; not because he had wanted their company but because being seen with them had helped to maintain the camouflage that he was fancy-free. Yet every evening spent with another woman had been a wasted one, making him realise that only one pair of lips could give him satisfaction, one slender body that could assuage his needs.

'I will never marry anyone except *you*,' he stated, and though he remained against the desk their eyes met in a look that was all-embracing.

'It would only be a business arrangement,' Gina insisted.

'Like hiring a secretary?'

'Exactly.'

'You can fire a secretary,' he said dryly.

'If you make a proper agreement with—with the right

22

person, you will also be able to end the marriage. Annul it,' she added quickly.

Luke could not help smiling. 'Darling Gina, you have no reason to be jealous of me! If I did marry a woman other than you, there would be no problem about annulment.' He reached out and caught her hand. 'You're the only woman I could ever bear to touch!'

'Darling,' she whispered, and leant against him, knowing that when he felt her close it was difficult for him to refuse her anything. 'Can't you see that this is the best way out? You could marry some suitable young woman who would go with you to all those boring functions you have to attend, and at the same time it would stop Charles's fears about us and cut the ground from under Roger's feet.'

'This suitable young woman would be doing quite a lot of things,' Luke said dryly. 'Allaying the fears of a so far unsuspecting husband; acting as my hostess on boring occasions and cutting away the ground from the feet of an ideological young man!'

'You're teasing me,' Gina reproached.

'It's only by teasing you that I can make this situation bearable. My marrying someone else is a pipe dream. I'll fix up to see Mark Watson tomorrow and——'

'Darling, don't, I have exactly the right girl in mind. I'm sure she'd be willing to do it and it would solve all our problems.'

If Gina's suggestion that he marry someone else on a temporary basis had surprised Luke, then hearing that she actually had a candidate for the position surprised him even more and, seeing his expression, Gina pressed home her advantage.

'It's a girl I knew when I was at boarding school. At least she was in her first year when I was in my last, but she was very sweet and helpful. She had a crush on me, I think— you know what schoolgirls are like!' Gina half smiled. 'We kept in touch after I left and met from time to time on birthdays and Christmas holidays. She helps me occasionally when I need a secretary, and if Charles and I do a lot of entertaining she sometimes lends a hand with the arrangements. She's an efficient little thing.'

'And what makes you think she'll be willing to sacrifice herself for *us*?'

'She needs the money.'

'Money?' Luke asked sharply.

'We would have to pay her for agreeing to marry you,' Gina explained. 'I thought we could offer her five thousand pounds on the day of the wedding and another five thousand pounds when the marriage is annulled.'

'Well, well,' Luke said softly. 'So I've finally come down to the necessity of buying a wife!'

'Oh, Luke!' Gina's eyes filled with angry tears. 'I'm trying to help you; to help both of us.'

'Darling, I'm sorry.' He pulled her into his arms. 'It's just that I can't take the idea seriously. I've thought of *you* as my wife for so long that marrying anyone else—even as a temporary arrangement—is unthinkable. But I *will* think about it,' he added, as he felt Gina stiffen. 'Tell me more about her.'

'There isn't much to tell. As I said, we went to the same school and she has always been fond of me.'

'I'm not surprised. I can just imagine you taking pity on some buck-toothed little junior. I bet you were the most beautiful girl in your school.'

'I never thought about my looks then,' Gina lied, 'though I don't think Emily ever had buck teeth.'

Luke chuckled. 'If I know anything about women, then the one you've chosen for me probably looks like the back of a bus!'

'I certainly wouldn't choose you a beautiful wife,' Gina agreed with aplomb. 'But I wouldn't choose you an ugly one either: after all, there has to be a logical reason for your wanting to get married.'

'Even ugly girls find themselves husbands,' Luke counselled. 'You set too much store by appearances.'

'Would you love me if you didn't think me beautiful?'

'The question is academic.' His arms tightened their hold

24

of her. 'I wouldn't love you if you were a fool either.' He buried his head in the soft, faintly perfumed waves of her hair. 'I want to marry *you*,' he said fiercely. 'How can you expect me to think of anyone else?'

'At least agree to meet her,' Gina persisted. 'She's coming to the house tonight. She is organising some bazaar in the village where she lives and I promised her some clothes. I know Charles has asked you to dinner and it would give you an opportunity to see her.'

Luke sighed and accepted the fact that Gina was in no mood for his kisses. 'What makes you so sure this girl would agree to marry me? I know the money is a considerable attraction, but even so . . .'

'The money would be the main attraction. She wants it for a man.'

The faint liking Luke had experienced for this unknown girl who loved Gina evaporated at these words. Why on earth did she need money for a man? Was it a boy-friend who required assistance or did she consider herself so plain that she wanted a dowry to buy herself a husband?

'Please meet her,' Gina pleaded, and Luke found himself agreeing. It was easier to stand up to an irate board of directors than to remain firm in front of those beseeching blue eyes.

'Tell Charles I can't make dinner,' he said. 'I told him this morning I was hoping to take my lawyer to my club to iron out a few details of my new contract. Though perhaps it might be as well to delay that,' he concluded dryly.

'Don't delay anything,' Gina said sharply. 'Meet Emily first and *then* decide what to do.'

'Very well.' He caught the rose-tipped hand and held it against his face. 'When will I see you? Alone, I mean?'

'I don't know. We have to settle this with Roger first. At the moment I'd be scared for us to meet. Try and understand how I feel, Luke. I don't want to hurt Charles.'

'Nor do I,' he said soberly.

'Then I'll see you tonight at the house,' she whispered,

and went quickly from the room before he had a chance to change his mind.

Emily Lamb jumped down from the bus as it stopped at the traffic lights, ignoring the warning of the conductor who said it was not a proper stop, and set off briskly along Park Lane towards Grosvenor Street. The one-way traffic speeding remorselessly on her right detracted from the calm elegance of the buildings that reared skywards on her left, though the elegance returned as she swung down a side turning. During the day the traffic was thick here too, but when the shops in Oxford Street and Bond Street closed, it came into its own original eighteenth-century charm, so that it was hard to believe that the graceful houses with their shallow steps and glass fanlights above the narrow front doors were the offices of public companies and not the private homes for which purpose they had originally been built. Yet one house in Grosvenor Street still existed as such, and it was here that Charles Harrick lived, as his father and father's father had done before him.

Emily mounted the steps and rang the bell, the more firmly because she always felt as nervous as a schoolgirl when she came here. It was a throwback to the past when Gina had been very much the head girl and she herself very much the junior.

'Good evening, Jackson,' Emily greeted the elderly butler as she stepped into the dark, marble-floored hall. 'Mrs. Harrick is expecting me.'

The butler nodded and took her coat and she went up the stairs, past the first floor and the drawing-room to the second floor with its two master bedrooms, each with its own sitting-room and bathroom. It was the suite on the left that she entered, and she stopped as she saw Gina was not there.

'I'll be with you in a moment,' Gina called. 'I got back late and I'm still changing. Help yourself to a drink.'

Emily shook her head, then remembering she could not be seen, said 'No,' in a light yet firm voice. 'I've typed all your letters,' she added. 'Where are the new ones?'

26

'On the desk. But don't bother with them yet. I want to talk to you first.'

Emily wandered over to look at the stack of open envelopes on the Sheraton desk, then remembering Gina's injunction, went over to look at a pile of the latest novels stacked on one of the tables. They were American editions, their lurid covers indicative of their lurid contents. With a grimace she left them untouched and wandered over to the window. The room overlooked a small garden. It was too small to be a garden proper, and in the summer was filled with tubs of exotic flowers. Now it was shrouded in November gloom and she stepped back from the chilly pane and saw herself dimly reflected in it.

Not that a mirror proper would have given her a much brighter reflection, she thought wryly, for she was a dark, winsome-looking girl, standing not more than five feet tall with a small, delicately boned frame, very pale complexion and jet black hair that fell thick and straight to her shoulders. Her nose was slightly tip-tilted and her chin, though small, was firm and determined. Her brow was wide and marked only by dark, winged eyebrows above slanting grey eyes. Her eyes were her most beautiful feature, and because they gave away so much of her thoughts she generally kept her lids half lowered, a habit she had learned during her mutinous years at boarding school. There was a childish roundness to her cheeks which was echoed by her small full mouth with its babyish short upper lip, below which one caught the gleam of small white teeth. Taken singly, each feature showed a particular facet of her character, but put together they did not quite meld, so that each change of mood brought a change of facial expression; one moment puckish the next provocative; one moment gamine the next sad. Too much sadness, she thought heavily. Since her parents' untimely death, which had occurred the year before she had left school, there had been little about her life to make her happy.

Gina's entry was a welcome interruption to her unpleasant memories and Emily greeted her with a warm smile.

How surprised Gina would be to know that she saw through her charm to the selfishness that lay beneath it; she would have been even more surprised to know that Emily liked her because of it, admiring the ruthless tenacity with which she achieved what she wanted.

'Forgive me for being so long.' Gina's unusually warm tone warned Emily that a favour was soon to be asked.

'I hope you don't want me to fill a place at one of your boring dinner parties?'

'Darling, how can you call them boring? Some of the most interesting people in London come here.'

'It takes more than a fat bank account to make people interesting to *me*.'

'I swear to heaven you're a secret socialist!'

'Not such a secret one,' Emily grinned, and looked more gamine than ever, standing there in her serviceable navy dress with its neat Peter Pan collar and cuffs.

'Don't you have something more sophisticated to wear?' Gina asked. 'You look about fifteen in that get-up.'

'Beggars can't be choosers,' Emily retorted, and added quickly: 'Don't offer to lend me any money, because you know I'll refuse.'

'More fool you. If you prefer to give your money to that no-good cousin of yours, then——'

'Clive has been like a brother to me,' Emily interrupted.

'Just because you grew up with him——' Gina made herself stop, realising that to minimise the girl's loyalty to her cousin was exactly the opposite of what she wanted to do, for it was on this loyalty that she was counting for the success of her plans. 'Any hope of Clive paying off his debts?'

'Not unless a miracle happens within the next couple of months.'

'And if it doesn't?'

'Then he'll go to prison. The auditors start examining the company's books after Christmas, and Clive says they will spot the discrepancy within a few weeks.'

'So unless he can replace that five thousand pounds, they

will discover that he stole it?'

'He didn't steal it,' Emily protested, 'he borrowed it to invest in the stock market.'

'There's a nasty name for people who do that with other people's money,' Gina said. 'Your cousin is a thief, and not a very clever one either. But if you're so crazy about him that you're willing to live like a church mouse in order to give him every penny you have . . .'

'He was wonderful to my parents,' Emily said matter-of-factly, 'and wonderful to me when they died. It wasn't easy for him to be saddled with a weepy seventeen-year-old, and he paid for me to finish my education.'

'You've more than repaid him for that.'

'I don't think you can ever repay a person for their kindness. You have to go on doing it.'

'Better you than me,' Gina shrugged. 'But then I'm not the self-sacrificing type.' She drifted across the room in a cloud of pale pink chiffon. It was a difficult colour for Gina to wear, yet it enhanced the fairness of her red-gold hair and gave it a softness that was infinitely flattering to her skin. Looking at her, Emily wished that she too could be the possessor of such chocolate box beauty, and with a pang pushed the thought aside.

'You said you wanted to talk to me, Gina.'

'I do. Sit down and relax. What I have to say will take a little time.' The beautifully curved mouth trembled. 'You've heard me speak of Luke Adams?'

'The magnate of Moorgate?'

Gina ignored the sarcasm. 'He needs your help. Charles has asked him to become Managing Director; it will be announced officially tomorrow. Naturally I'm delighted about it, for it takes a lot of the responsibility away from Charles. Eventually I'm hoping that Charles will resign completely.'

'He should have done so ages ago. It isn't as if he needs the money.'

'Men like Charles don't work for money,' Gina smiled. 'They do it for prestige and power.'

'Then they're mad.' Emily gave a shake of her head. 'Do go on; I'm sorry I interrupted you.'

'I was telling you about Luke. In his new position he will have to do a great deal of entertaining—people from abroad, financiers—and he'll need someone to help him.'

'Well, there's no problem in that. I'm quite willing to do so as long as he doesn't expect me to be on call every single weekend.'

'This isn't just a weekend job,' Gina said. 'It's a full-time one. Luke isn't looking for a social secretary, Emily, he wants a wife.'

'Am I supposed to do the interviewing for him?' Emily asked, attempting to be funny because she could not believe she had heard correctly.

'Oh, do be serious,' Gina's nerves were beginning to play her false. 'I'm faced with an awful problem and I'm counting on you to help me out of it.'

Emily stared at her friend, realising that she was deadly serious. 'If Mr. Adams wants to get married, I don't see why it should be a problem for *you*.'

'But he doesn't want to get married! That's part of the worry. It's a question of his *having* to do so.'

'Does he know you're asking me to fill the vacancy?' Emily demanded. 'Or is this something you've dreamed up by yourself?'

'Of course he knows. Luke isn't the sort of man that you can tell what to do. We discussed it together this afternoon.'

'And you both decided that I was a suitable candidate?'

'*I* decided it and Luke has agreed to meet you—providing you're willing to see him, of course.'

'Of course,' Emily said dryly. 'But first of all tell me why this highly successful and clever man—he must be clever or Charles wouldn't have asked him to be his Managing Director—hasn't been clever enough to find his own lady-love?'

'He's been too concerned with his career.'

'I'm sure he could find someone suitable if he took a few

30

days off,' Emily said sarcastically. 'Honestly, Gina, you must be crazy to think I'd agree to such a thing. I don't know the man, and from the little bit you've told me about him, I don't even like him!'

'You'd like him very much if you met him. He's coming here this evening to see you, as a matter of fact.'

'Then he'll have a wasted journey.'

'He's coming to see Charles too.'

'Then it won't be such a wasted journey!'

'Oh, Emily,' Gina said in exasperation. 'And I thought you wanted to help Clive?'

'What has Clive got to do with it?'

'He needs five thousand pounds, doesn't he? And that's what Luke will pay you if you become his wife—with another five thousand pounds on the day your marriage is annulled.'

Emily was glad she was sitting down, otherwise she would have fallen. 'Did you say five thousand pounds?'

'Yes. Five when you marry Luke and five when your marriage is ended. He will only need you to—he will only need a wife for a couple of years, possibly less. That's why it's important for him to choose someone who will be willing to step out of the limelight and back—to——'

'Obscurity,' Emily finished.

'To a more humdrum existence,' Gina said tactfully. 'You could have five thousand pounds by this time next week. Think of it, Emily.'

'I am thinking.' Emily jumped up and moved round the room, her steps so light that they barely seemed to touch the carpet, her hair swinging round her shoulders like black silk. 'But why so much money, and why *me*?'

'The money because it's a business transaction, and *you*, because you were the first girl that came to my mind. You would be in a position of great trust with Luke and it's important for him to have confidence in your discretion. After all, as his wife you'll probably hear a lot of things that many people would give their eye-teeth to know.' Gina looked at her fingers and thoughtfully twirled one of her diamond rings. 'Actually I thought of you because of Clive. Five thousand pounds would stop him going to prison.'

Emily ran the tip of her tongue over her lips. 'And you said Mr. Adams was coming here this evening?'

'Yes.' Gina relaxed, knowing she had achieved the most difficult part of what she had set out to do. To finally convince Luke that he must use Emily as a cover would be far less difficult. 'There's only you and I for dinner,' she murmured. 'I've persuaded Charles to have it in his room and then afterwards we can go and sit with him until Luke arrives.'

'To inspect me,' Emily said.

'I should imagine Luke thinks the same way about you.'

'I don't see why. *He's* the one who wants to get married.'

'It isn't a matter of wanting to, darling. It's a necessity. He loves his freedom.' Gina paused. 'Freedom is extremely important to him. He wouldn't expect his marriage to tie him down.'

'I couldn't care less what he does with his time. I would be there when he needs me and have my own life to live when he doesn't—*if* I decided to go ahead with it, that is—and I'm by no means sure.'

Gina lowered her eyelids to hide the triumph in her eyes. Emily would accept Luke; there was no doubt of that. All she had to do now was to get Luke to make the proposal. 'Let's go and eat,' she said affectionately, and linked her arm with the younger girl.

CHAPTER THREE

EMILY always enjoyed her meals in Gina's home. It was a pleasure to eat food she had not prepared herself, and even more pleasurable to eat luxuries she normally only read about. Tonight's dinner was no exception, and delicate consommé was followed by fillet steaks nestling on a bed of sweetcorn, followed by fresh raspberries flown in from heaven knew where and home-made cream. Gina ate sparingly, but Emily tackled her food with gusto, happily accepting a second helping of fruit.

'For such a little thing you eat like a horse,' Gina commented. 'Aren't you worried about getting fat?'

'No.' Emily swallowed her last mouthful of raspberries and set down her spoon. 'And I don't know what you're worrying about either; you're as thin as a pin.' She gazed at Gina enviously. 'I wish your clothes fitted me. You have no idea how the women in the village fight over them in the bazaar.'

'You aren't fatter than I am, darling. I'm sure it's just a question of shortening them.'

'Probably,' Emily admitted. 'The real reason is that I wouldn't feel comfortable in them. I'd be like a sparrow dressed up in peacock feathers!'

Gina laughed. Emily always managed to put her in a good humour. It must be due to her droll similes and her ability to make a point in the nicest possible way. Yes, Emily would do very well for Luke. She was not so dull that she would drive him to find other female company when she herself was not free, nor was she sufficiently attractive to impinge upon him as a woman. Yes, little Emily Lamb was the ideal choice.

Almost purring with her satisfaction, Gina led the way to Charles's sitting-room. Despite not dining with them, he had changed into a dinner jacket and was reclining on the settee, a book in his hand, which he immediately put down as they came in. As always, Gina's behaviour was faultless, and she kissed him on the brow and gracefully sank into a chair beside him, acting as though she were the genuinely loving wife he believed her to be.

Watching the tableau, Emily marvelled at her friend's ability to maintain such an act, for though Gina was too loyal to discuss her marriage to Charles, it was evident that they only enjoyed a platonic relationship. Yet it was sufficiently satisfying for Gina to remain with him, and there was no doubt whatever that, for his part, Charles adored his young and beautiful wife. Did Gina ever feel she was wasting her life by remaining with a man old enough to be her father? Emily wondered, but as always, dismissed the question without finding an answer.

'And how is my second favourite woman?' Charles Harrick teased Emily as he held out his hands to her.

'All the better for seeing you.' She bent to kiss him. 'I read about you in the papers this morning.'

'I thought you didn't read the financial section?'

'I always read it when I know I'm coming here. It gives me something to talk about with you.'

'Gripe about, you mean,' he laughed. 'Come on now, tell me what I did wrong this time.'

'You didn't give a frank enough statement to the shareholders when you bought out their company.'

'What are you two talking about?' Gina asked.

'Emily is being very knowing about a little property company we recently acquired.'

'I would hardly call a million pounds' worth of assets little,' Emily murmured.

About to reply, Charles paused. 'I think I hear Luke's car.'

Gina crossed to the window and pulled back the curtain. 'You're right. He's just parked it.'

Emily forced herself to remain passive, and resolutely kept her eyes away from the door behind her as, a moment

34

later, she heard it open and a soft spoken voice said, 'Good evening.' Only as the owner of the voice moved past her chair to greet his host did she get her first sight of him. He was like a big, silver-blond bear, though he moved with infinitely more grace, as light on his feet as a boxer and with the same suggestion of controlled power that not even his well-tailored dinner jacket could disguise. He was still bent in greeting over Charles and she could not see his face, though she noticed that his hair was thick and straight and stopped short of his collar. Then he straightened and turned to be introduced to her, and she saw he was pale-skinned, with a controlled mouth and watchful eyes; dark grey, she thought them to be, but they were narrowed in speculation and she could not be sure of their colour.

'Good evening,' he said, and his grasp of her hand was firm, before he let it go and eased himself into a chair beside her. But he spoke to Charles, telling him what had taken place during his dinner with his solicitor, and though she tried to make sense of what he was saying, she was too conscious of his physical presence: of his height and the width of his shoulders; of his strong neck and vital, shining hair, and the light soft voice that was in direct contrast to the masculinity he exuded. Would she have been so overwhelmed by him under normal circumstances, or was it because she knew he had come here to inspect her with a view to marriage?

'I understand you and Gina were at school together?'

He was speaking directly to her for the first time, and she gathered her wits about her and nodded. 'Yes, we were.'

'Did she really wear a navy-blue gymslip or was it just a figment of her imagination?'

'We all wore gymslips,' Emily smiled, 'but Gina wore hers belted at the waist!'

'She was fashion-conscious even at that age,' Charles Harrick chuckled, 'and she's just as fashion-conscious now. She has been on the best-dressed list every year since I married her.'

'Gina is ideal to dress,' Emily said. 'I'd never be voted

35

best-dressed whatever I wore.'

'I don't see why you should be so deprecating about yourself,' Charles replied.

'Honesty isn't deprecating. You have to be tall to look elegant.'

Luke's surprise grew as he listened to this quaint young woman talk. She was unlike anything he had anticipated and definitely not the sort of girl he had expected to be a friend of Gina's. But she wasn't a friend exactly. Hadn't Gina said something about taking pity on her because of her circumstances?

'Perhaps you could give Emily a lift?' Gina's voice roused him from his thoughts.

'Of course,' he said promptly, and looked at the little dark-haired girl beside him. 'You don't mind if I have a few words alone with Charles first?'

He watched her as she nodded and went over to bid Charles goodnight. There was an old-fashioned air about the way she did so, though possibly this was caused as much by her dress as her manner. So this was Gina's choice for him, was it? Emily Lamb did not look like a girl who would cause trouble, and as such she might be exactly what he was looking for, provided he was going to do as Gina wished and get married after all. He shied away from the thought. He did not want to marry anyone except Gina. Lord, how he loved her.

'I'll wait downstairs for you, Mr. Adams,' Emily said, and he gave her an absent-minded smile before turning to Charles.

'Well?' Gina said to Emily as they went back to her sitting-room. 'Isn't he as charming as I said he was?'

'Are polar bears charming?' Emily smiled. 'And that's what he looks like to me.'

'I must tell Luke you see him as a bear,' Gina said with amusement.

'Don't tell him anything of the sort.'

'He won't mind.'

'But I will.'

36

'Does that mean you're going to consider what I asked you?'

Emily gave a noncommittal grunt. '*He* has to consider it too.'

'Luke needs a temporary wife,' Gina said firmly, 'and you need the money. It's an ideal arrangement.'

Some twenty minutes later they heard Luke bid Charles goodnight, and with a murmur Gina glided from the room. Left alone, Emily considered the position, her mind on Clive's predicament. Though disillusioned by what he had done, she still felt obligated to help him. His kindness to her when she had been most in need of it made this imperative. But until tonight—and Gina's incredible suggestion—she had seen no way of coming to his aid. But now a kindly fate was giving her a chance to do so, and two years of her life in exchange for Clive's good name and freedom seemed a small price to pay. The door opened and the object of this fate stood there, his coat over his arm.

'Are you ready to go?'

She jumped up and he held the door wide for her to pass in front of him. She saw Gina in the corridor and the three of them went down the stairs to the hall.

'Call me,' Gina said softly to Luke, and Emily saw the silver-blond head nod.

Gina's concern surprised her until she remembered how much it would benefit Charles to have a managing director whom he trusted implicitly in charge of the company to which he had given most of his life. At the thought of Charles some of Emily's repugnance at what she was planning lessened. If marriage to Luke Adams made Charles more content, it would be well worth doing, and made the mercenary aspect of the arrangement easier to bear. With a sigh she took the front seat of an opulent car.

'Where do you live?' he asked as they moved away from the kerb.

'Little Sutton, near Cambridge.' The car slackened speed as his foot came off the accelerator and she could not help a chuckle. 'But you don't have to drive me there tonight, Mr. Adams. I'm staying at a hostel near Regents Park.'

'That's a relief.' They quickened speed again. 'We have some things to talk over, but do you mind if we wait until I park somewhere? I prefer to concentrate on one thing at a time.'

'You give the impression of being able to concentrate on many things at the same time.'

'Part of my success lies in giving the wrong impression!' he said humorously, and lapsed into silence until he drew the car to a stop in a side turning. Then he swivelled round and surveyed her slowly.

She stared back at him with equal candour, noticing how the moonlight turned him into a beautiful black and silver image and knowing it did far less for her. 'I must look like a witch,' she thought, 'with my little face and black hair.'

'You're younger than I expected,' he said abruptly.

'I'm twenty-three. I look younger because I'm small.'

'It's more than size that makes you look young. I presume Gina has told you I want a wife?'

'She said you need one; that's different, isn't it?'

'Don't let's play with words,' he said brusquely. 'Are you willing or aren't you?'

'Are *you*?'

The question took him by surprise. 'I suppose I must be. If I weren't, I wouldn't be talking to you like this. It wasn't until today that I—that I realised I needed to get married. It means an entire readjustment of my thinking.'

'I'm sure it did,' she said carefully. 'But if you want to become Managing Director of Harricks, I don't suppose you'll mind having to make some sacrifice.'

His head tilted sharply. 'I don't consider it would be a sacrifice to marry you, Miss Lamb. For your age you appear to be an eminently sensible young woman.'

'How old are *you*, Mr. Adams?'

If he was startled, he did not show it. 'Thirty-three. But far older than that in experience.'

'Gina said it would be for two years,' Emily murmured.

'That is merely an approximate time.'

'Will you be giving up the Managing Directorship after that?'

'I hope not.'

'Then why will you only need a wife for two years? I'm sorry to be so curious, but I like to get things straight.'

'And very sensible of you to do so. But let's say I only see my social life as being a problem for the next couple of years.' He hesitated. 'I believe Gina has spoken to you about the financial arrangements?'

'Yes. Five thousand pounds the day I marry you and five thousand on the day we get divorced. It's a large sum of money.'

'I expect good service for it,' he stated.

'You don't mean——'

'By service, I mean the social side of marriage, not the physical.'

Her cheeks burned and she was angry for having asked such a question. She should have known that a man like Luke Adams would not need to buy his love. Her curiosity stirred and the question she had asked Gina came forcibly to mind. How was it that a man of such obvious good looks and virility was not already married? Somehow the excuse of no time and too much work did not ring true.

'What's worrying you, Miss Lamb?'

His question made her realise he had not achieved his present position through lack of brains. 'I was wondering why you aren't married already.'

'I have no secret vice that has prevented me from marriage,' he said dryly. 'So you can set your mind at rest on that score.'

'Then why couldn't you find your own girl?'

'I haven't even started to look for one. The necessity only arose today, and Gina immediately suggested you. She said you need the money as much as I need a wife, and also that you are trustworthy and discreet and won't mind being bought off when I no longer need you.'

The brutal candour of the words left her breathless.

'You're very forthright, Mr. Adams.'

'I like honesty,' he said, and then added: 'Whenever possible.' He moved slightly and one side of his face was silvered by the moonlight. 'Well, Emily Lamb, are you willing to come to the slaughter?'

'A remark like that is enough to make me say no.'

'Sorry. I promise not to do it again!'

'I bet you will.'

'Not if you marry me. Then you'll be Emily Adams.'

'Good heavens, so I will. Emily Adams. It doesn't sound very imposing. Still, I'm not a very imposing-looking person.'

'You will suit me admirably.'

'You're taking me on trust,' she persisted. 'I might have a terrible temper or eat my peas with a knife.'

'You went to a good boarding school,' he shrugged, 'and Gina tells me you've acted as her social secretary from time to time. Don't minimise yourself, Miss Lamb. I dislike people who do.'

'I'm sorry, Mr. Adams.'

'You'd better make it Luke.'

'I'll try to remember.' She waited, expecting him to say more, and was disappointed when he switched on the ignition and started to drive away.

Following her instructions he drew up opposite the hostel and switched off the ignition. 'How will Friday week suit you, Emily?'

'Suit me?'

'For getting married.'

'So soon?'

'There's no reason for us to wait, is there?'

'Oh no, the quicker I marry you the quicker I can get...' Her voice trailed away and she was aware of him looking at her with the first sign of curiosity.

'You must need the money very badly if you're willing to marry a stranger in order to get it. Gina said it was for a man.'

'Yes. I have to—— If it weren't for that, I would never

40

have agreed to your proposal.'

'Does he mean that much to you?'

'Yes,' she said stiltedly.

Luke leaned forward. 'Are you selling *yourself* in order to buy *him*?'

She caught her breath at the implication. 'That's a horrid thing to say!'

'I thought you liked frankness.'

'Not when it's cruel.'

'I don't mean to be cruel. Put it down to curiosity.'

'Then I don't intend to satisfy it. This is a business arrangement, Mr. Adams. Let's keep it that way.'

'As you wish.' He opened his door and, despite the speed with which she opened hers, was walking beside her up the steps to the hostel. 'There's only one other thing we have to talk about,' he said. 'Charles Harrick. I would like him to think we're getting married for the usual reasons.'

She stared up at him, having to tilt her head right back to do so. 'How can he? We've only met tonight!'

'Don't you believe in love at first sight, Emily Lamb?'

'You're obviously hoping Charles does!'

His smile indicated his appreciation of her quick reply. 'I'll phone you and give you a date for lunch this week,' he said. 'There are a few things to discuss before we get married.' He touched her arm with light but firm fingers. 'Thank you for agreeing. I don't think either of us will regret it.'

She watched him go down the steps to his car and was still standing there as he drove away. What on earth had she let herself in for? It was a question she was to ask herself many times in the future, but at this moment she had no prescience of the anguish the answer would give her.

CHAPTER FOUR

EMILY met Luke for lunch on Friday afternoon, a week before the date he had arranged for their wedding. He took her to Claridges, a prosaic though expensive choice, and one which made her aware of her unfashionable tweed coat and dress. But perhaps this tall, commanding-looking man was not fashion-conscious. After all, if he was too busy to find his own wife, he might be too busy to notice what she wore!

'You will need to buy some clothes,' he said, interrupting her thoughts and immediately making nonsense of them. 'I suggest you let Gina help you.'

'I won't deck myself out in pink ostrich feathers!' she retorted.

He looked momentarily put out and then reluctantly smiled. 'I thought she would be able to tell you the right places to go.'

'When you have enough money there's no problem finding the right places.'

'Don't worry, you'll have more than enough money.'

'I wasn't hinting,' she said quickly.

'I know that. As I told you before, Miss Lamb—I really must remember to call you Emily—as I told you before, Emily, I appreciate your honesty. I have enough subterfuge in my business life without having to mince words in my private one.'

'What exactly will I be expected to do, Luke?' She was delighted at how casually she managed to say his name, giving no indication of the effort it cost her. It was ridiculous that he could make her so self-conscious, it must be due to his physique. He made all the men around him look like pigmies. There was obviously Nordic blood in him somewhere, for he had the fearless look of a Norseman and a strong face that was at variance with the gentle voice.

Which was indicative of the real man? There was no point asking him and no point in looking to herself for the answer. He was a total mystery to her.

'I'll expect you to run my home.' His words forced her back to what he was saying. 'If you aren't tied up after lunch, I suggest we go and look at it.'

'Why? I'm sure you won't want me to do any redecorating.'

'Gina has invited us to have dinner with them tomorrow night, and it might be a good idea to let Charles know you've been to my flat.'

She blushed. 'Do you want him to think we're lovers?'

He looked nonplussed, then he chuckled. 'I think my request for honesty is going to rebound on my head! Are you always so outspoken?'

'It's my one failing.' She waited for him to say it was a virtue, but he did not do so, and instead picked up the menu and studied it. She did the same and not until they had given their order did he speak personally again. 'I want Charles to get the impression we're seeing a great deal of each other. After all, if we're going to get married in a week's time . . .'

'When are you going to tell him?'

'Some time next week.'

'Why can't he know the truth about our marriage?'

'No one must know. Don't question me about it, Emily, just take my word for it.'

'I have no intention of questioning you,' she said calmly. 'I'm not sufficiently interested in your private affairs.'

'Hey there! That remark was below the belt.'

'I didn't know Queensberry rules applied to the City!'

'And that's another one below the belt! But may I remind you that our arrangement is a personal one, not a City transaction.'

Melon and prosciutto was set before them and she picked up her spoon and fork and began to eat. 'This is *super*,' she murmured. 'I adore melon.'

'Good. They do a super rice pudding, too!'

43

She glanced at him beneath her lashes but decided to ignore the remark.

After lunch they drove—with a chauffeur this time—to Luke's flat, an opulently furnished one off St. James's. It was on the top floor of a new block, with a terrace on two sides of it that gave them a wonderful view of London. The furniture was Heal's, though there were one or two good pictures on the walls.

'You aren't very interested in your home, are you?' she commented.

'It's somewhere to sleep.'

'It will have to be more than that if we're supposed to be doing any social entertaining.'

'Social entertaining?'

'Isn't that why you're getting married?'

He nodded quickly. 'If you wish to make any alterations, by all means do so.'

'Would you like me to ask Gina first?'

'Don't be sarcastic with me, Emily.'

'I wasn't being sarcastic,' she said truthfully. 'I have my own ideas when it comes to clothes, but I know nothing about decor.'

'I'm sure you can manage on your own. Don't ask Gina.'

'I would only want to alter a few things,' she said, looking round. 'I'd like some more easy chairs and a bit more colour in the room. It's all rather dull.'

'For a girl who favours navy and white and brown tweed...'

'Wait till you see me in the expensive new clothes I intend to buy with all your money!'

He laughed. 'I'm glad you aren't embarrassed to talk about money.' He looked as though he were about to say more, then stopped and glanced at his watch. Taking the hint, she went to the door ahead of him and he followed her to the lift.

'I'll collect you tomorrow night,' he said suddenly. 'It will look better if we arrive at Gina's together.'

The last part of his sentence took away the pleasure from

the first part and she was surprised with herself for noticing it. Luke had made it quite clear that their relationship was a business one, and it was silly of her to regard it differently.

Yet despite reminding herself that she was marrying him solely in order to help Clive, she could not restrain a thrill of anticipation as she waited for him to collect her at the hostel the following evening. In expectancy of the allowance she would be getting from him, she had dipped into her savings and bought a new dinner dress, but the blue silk jersey could have been her navy wool for all the comment it drew from him as she came towards him, her coat around her shoulders, and she was angry with herself for being hurt by his disinterest. He looked even more good-looking than she had remembered, and was again wearing a dinner jacket, though this one was in wine velvet that turned his blond hair to silver. He was driving himself again too, and she was glad that the car was warm, for the only coat she could wear over such an elaborate dress was a lightweight one.

'You must buy a couple of furs,' he commented as though divining her thoughts.

'Velvet is equally glamorous and considerably cheaper.'

'Mink,' he replied. 'Though on second thoughts perhaps ermine or seal. Mink might overwhelm you.'

'You sound extremely knowledgeable about furs.'

'We made a take-over bid for a fur company last year, and I always make it my business to know as much as I can about any company we buy.'

She slewed round and looked at him. 'What did you do before you worked for Charles?'

'I lectured in Economics at Cambridge.'

'Good heavens!'

'Most people are surprised,' he conceded. 'Not because I was a don but because I've been a success in the business world. Mind you, I am a graduate of the Harvard Business School too, so that helps.'

'How could you bear to give up the academic life for the

rat race?'

'These particular rats live better!'

'So you sold your soul for money.'

'You're doing the same.'

She went scarlet. 'Only for two years, Mr. Adams.'

'Luke,' he reminded her, 'and smile at me lovingly to-night.'

'Don't worry, Luke darling, I'll kill you with love!'

He chuckled. 'I bet you would too.'

He still seemed amused by her remark when they entered the marble hall and climbed the stairs to the drawing-room. There were several people already present and Charles, giving no indication of his bad heart, was chatting with a group of men as they came in.

'How lovely that you were free to come,' he greeted Emily, and she was aware of him looking at her with faint surprise, as if he could not understand why Luke had chosen to bring *her* with him as his dinner guest.

Occasionally throughout the evening she saw him fling her a puzzled look, though now she knew it was due to Luke's behaviour towards her. It could by no means be called lover-like—he was far too careful for that—but the way he remained by her side and occasionally allowed his hand to rest on her arm indicated that their relationship was considerably more than casual. Even knowing it to be an act did not stop her from being warmed by his attentions, particularly since she was aware of the envious glances cast by the other women in the room. She wondered if Luke felt she compared well with them, and tried to gain some comfort from her new dress. But against Gina's superbly cut black velvet it looked dull and ordinary, and she could see why Luke had not commented on her appearance when he had collected her tonight. In a country pond she might be the goldfish, but in a London pool like this she was a veritable minnow.

'Wake up, sleepyhead.' Luke's voice was soft in her ear as he bent over her chair.

'Forgive me,' she apologised, quickly lifting her lids, 'but

I was up at five o'clock this morning.'

'How come?'

'We're holding a bazaar in the village and I promised to organise it. I'd planned to work on it all day, but coming here tonight meant I had to leave early.'

'So you started at the crack of dawn to make up the time? No wonder you're tired.' He hoisted her gently to her feet, keeping her hands in his as they went over to say goodnight to Charles and Gina.

'I hear it's all settled,' Gina whispered as Emily drew close.

'Yes. We're getting married next Friday.'

'I know. I haven't told Charles yet because Luke thought it better not to make it look such a rush. Have you told Clive about the money?'

Emily nodded, aware of Luke standing next to her and not sure whether he could hear what was being said.

'He must have been very pleased,' Gina persisted.

'Very,' Emily said stiffly, and was glad when Luke moved towards the door.

'Who is Clive?' he asked as they drove away from the house.

'You heard?'

'I can lip-read.'

'I'd better watch out for you, then.'

'Answer me, Emily.'

'I thought our personal lives were our own.'

'From next Friday onwards you share your personal life with mine, and it will remain that way for as long as we're married.'

'That cuts both ways.'

He caught his breath, but when he spoke his voice was as calm as before. 'I have no private life. Now then, is Clive the man for whom you need the money?'

'Yes.'

'Why does he require it?'

'For his—for his business. He's an accountant.'

'I see.'

47

She knew that he didn't, and waited nervously for his next question. But when it came it surprised her.

'You must care a great deal for this Clive if you're marrying me in order to give him five thousand pounds?'

'I do care for him. We grew up together. He's my third cousin.'

'But not so far removed emotionally?'

'We grew up together,' she repeated. 'I look on him as my brother.'

'You're certainly a loving sister to be giving him so much money. But you still haven't told me why he needs it so badly.'

Ashamed to tell the truth, she said the first thing that came into her head. 'I *want* him to have it. I'll always do anything for Clive. He means more to me than anyone else.'

'I see.' They drove for a while in silence before he spoke again. 'There's no need to get upset. I merely wanted to establish what your relationship was with him. Now I know, the subject is closed.'

'He isn't in love with me.' This was one thing she was determined to make clear.

'That is obvious. You wouldn't be giving him five thousand pounds if he was.'

She rounded on him furiously. 'I am *not* buying him! If he doesn't get that money, he'll ... He needs it in order to expand.'

'Are you sure he'll wait two years for you?'

She clenched her hands and resolutely refused to answer. If Luke persisted in misunderstanding her she was not going to quarrel with him about it. They completed the drive to the hostel in silence and, as he had done on the first night he had driven her home, he escorted her to the door.

'We have a few more things to talk over before we get married,' Luke said. 'And I think——'

'If you've changed your mind because of Clive, I quite understand,' she interrupted.

'Of course I haven't changed my mind.' He gave her a little shake. 'You silly child, you can do what you like with the money I give you. I'm only concerned that you don't make a fool of yourself. I'd have thought you'd like to spend some of the money on your cottage. Or do you intend selling it?'

'Oh no. How could I? I mean at the end—when our marriage is over—I'll go back there to live.'

'Perhaps we can go down there for the odd weekend,' he said. 'I always wanted a place in the country.'

'I thought you would already have a mansion.'

'That's for married men with families.'

She sensed the sadness in his voice and longed to tell him she would try to give him the companionship he seemed to lack. But unexpected shyness kept her silent and she merely gave him her hand and said goodnight.

'Don't forget you're spending the weekend with me in the country,' he reminded her. 'The Robertsons asked me to bring you.'

'Was that the thin couple Charles was talking to for such a long time?'

'Yes. He is chairman of a company we're interested in buying. The weekend will be an excuse for us to have a little exploratory chat about it.'

'Do you never do anything for purely social reasons?'

'Of course I do.' There was a slight pause. 'I *am* human, you know.'

'Yes,' Emily thought to herself, 'you certainly are,' and wished she could have met him under normal circumstances. How exciting it would have been. A man of such good looks and personality had never come into her life before. But then there were not many men like Luke Adams —and thank goodness for that, for if there were, there would be many wet eyes and broken hearts.

'What deep thoughts are going on behind that wide white brow of yours?' he enquired, and she flashed him such a brilliant smile that he was suddenly aware of the gamine quality about her. He had always thought of her as a sparrow. No, that wasn't true. Her hair was too dark and glossy for that. A raven perhaps, or with those shining eyes possibly a magpie.

'What are *your* deep thoughts?' she countered.

'I asked *you* that question first! But just to show you how magnanimous I am, I'll admit I was thinking you are more like a magpie or a raven than a sparrow.'

'Woe!' she said with irony. 'You couldn't stretch yourself and see me as a mouse?'

'I've paid you a compliment,' he said firmly. 'Birds are lovely creatures, delicate and full of interest, provided you have the patience to watch them. But now I've answered *your* question, I expect you to answer mine.'

'I've forgotten what it was.'

'I had the impression you were coming to some deduction about me and I was curious to know what it was.'

She hesitated and then decided to be truthful. In a situation like theirs, honesty was the only thing they could offer each other. 'I was thinking what a good thing it was that you've been preoccupied with your work; otherwise you would have gone around breaking a great many hearts.'

'I haven't been a celibate,' he said abruptly. 'Don't let Gina kid you that I am.'

'She hasn't spoken of you to me.'

'That's a relief. When two women start to dissect a man they don't leave much of him whole!'

'There speaks a frightened male,' she laughed. 'I never thought you would care what anybody said about you.'

'I don't.'

'Armoured in your own invincibility,' she murmured, and heard him catch his breath. But his next words were a complete change of subject.

'I will collect you on Friday evening between four and five. That should give us plenty of time to get to the Robertsons.' He eyed her. 'The women generally wear long clothes in the evening and tweeds or trousers during the day.'

'I do know how the rich live,' she rejoined.

'No offence meant, Miss Prickly Pear.'

'None taken, sir.' She waved her hand at him and walked

into the hostel, waiting in the foyer until she heard the sound of his car dying away. Again she wished she had had the opportunity to meet him under normal circumstances. Yet in normal circumstances she would probably never have met him, for their social orbits were too different. It was incredible to think she would be spending the next couple of years as his wife, pretending they had a normal marriage. It was a frightening thought, and only the knowledge that by doing it she was helping Clive prevented her from telephoning him there and then and saying she had changed her mind. 'I must be suffering from pre-wedding nerves,' she mused. 'I have the chance of earning a small fortune, and I'd be crazy to turn it down.'

Upstairs in her room she surveyed her blue dress as she took it off and hung it in the wardrobe. Luke had not liked it. His lack of comment had been indicative of that, for had it met with his approval she was sure he would have said so. She took out the dress again and held it in front of her as she looked at herself in the mirror. She had spent far more on it than she normally did, but in comparison with the dresses worn at the party tonight this one was cheap-looking. Unaccountably depressed, she flung it on to a chair and got into bed. Trousers and tweeds and a couple of long dresses for the weekend, Luke had told her. Well, he was going to be in for an uncomfortable surprise if he thought her wardrobe could run to that. The only long dress she possessed was this blue one, and as for tweeds and trousers ... She smiled as she considered her serviceable navy suit and the couple of pairs of dungarees she owned. Not that she normally cared about her appearance, except for a foolish and illogical wish to be able to look sufficiently glamorous to make a pair of male eyes look at her with appreciation. Any male eyes, she told herself firmly, not one pair in particular.

Emily overslept in the morning, a luxury she rarely allowed herself. But she was staying in London to do some work for Gina, who was giving a large dinner party during the weekend and wished her to arrange the menu and do all the ordering for it. It was this that made her realise Gina and Charles would not be at the Robertsons' during the weekend. It was unnerving to think this would be the first time she would be alone with Luke. Still, it was something she must get used to, for once she was his wife there would be many such times. She must even get used to being alone with him without the benefit of casual friends around them.

'There's a letter for you, Miss Lamb.' The woman at the reception desk called her as she came into the foyer after breakfast.

Surprised, Emily took it, and saw it had been delivered by hand. The writing was heavy and bold and instinctively she knew it was Luke's. With shaking fingers she slit the envelope and took out a single sheet of thick notepaper. As she unfolded it, something fluttered to the floor and picking it up she saw it was a cheque for five hundred pounds. Heart hammering, she read the letter.

'After I left you last night,' he wrote, 'I realised you might be short of cash. When you are my wife I will expect you to dress accordingly, so I hope you won't object if I jump the gun by a few days and give you a cheque now. If it isn't enough, don't hesitate to let me know. We will have to talk about a proper dress allowance for you when we meet, but in the meantime enjoy yourself with this.' Then came his signature, simply written without any of the flourishes she had expected.

She folded the letter and put it together with the cheque in her handbag. If all the money she had spent on clothes in the past five years were added up she doubted if it would amount to the sum Luke had sent her this morning, and this, more than anything else that had yet transpired, showed her how different their life-styles were. Somehow it boded ill for their future, and she wondered if it would be better to tell Luke she could not go ahead and marry him. Yet the reasons for which she had accepted his proposition were as important today as they had been a week ago, and because of this she forced herself to walk past the telephone booth and out into the street.

It would have been nice to have been able to return Luke's cheque and say she did not need it, but it would also have been foolhardy, and Emily was nothing if not practical. Too practical, sometimes she thought, for men seemed to prefer women who were foolish and illogical rather than those who knew where they were going. Not that she herself had gone very far in her twenty-three years.

Village life wasn't conducive to great happenings. It was a pity she had listened to Clive and stayed in the old cottage. But he enjoyed his occasional weekends there so much that she had not had the heart to sell it and move to London, nor even to rent it and accept the offer of living in Gina's house as her social secretary. Not that she regretted that particular decision. She admired Gina, but she was not blind to her selfishness, and she knew that though Gina was nice to work for on a part-time basis, she would be too demanding as a full-time employer.

She paused by the bus stop, and because there was none in sight she resumed walking. She was intensely aware of the cheque in her handbag and toyed with the idea of using the morning for window-shopping. Yet there were other things that had to be done first, most important of them being to see Clive. She had already told him there was a possibility of her getting the five thousand pounds he needed, and he had been so speechless with relief that he had not questioned her as to where or how she could find such an amount. But his questions would come sooner or later, and deciding to make it sooner, she went into a phone box and called him.

An hour later they sat opposite each other in a quiet café a hundred yards from the company where he worked, while she carefully explained her reasons for agreeing to marry Luke Adams.

'You're out of your mind!' Clive exploded when she had finished. 'I know I'm desperate for the money, but I can't let you sacrifice your life in order to get it for me. The man must be a maniac!'

'Don't be silly,' she protested. 'He's a very respected and

clever businessman.'

'He might be the opposite in his private life.'

'I won't be sharing his private life—at least not in that way. I'll be acting as his hostess and taking care of his home.'

'Couldn't he get a housekeeper to do that?'

'You can't take a housekeeper with you when you travel, and you can't let her entertain your guests.'

'I still think it odd that he can't find a wife in the normal way.'

'Perhaps it's because he doesn't want a normal sort of marriage,' Emily said quietly. 'I get the impression that he doesn't believe in love—that he's only marrying because he has to do so.'

'When is it supposed to be?'

'Friday week.'

'I don't like it,' Clive repeated. 'And I won't let you do it.'

'You can't stop me. I've already given him my word and I don't intend to break it.'

'Does he know why you've agreed to such a scheme?' Clive asked.

'I've told him I want the money to help a cousin of mine. I haven't said why you need it and Luke assumed I—that I——' She stopped, too embarrassed to explain Luke's conclusions. But the discomfiture on Clive's face was even more embarrassing for her, and she said quickly: 'I didn't say anything about your borrowing company money. Luke thinks I'm using the five thousand to buy your love.'

'My *what*?'

'He thinks I'm in love with you, and that I believe that if I had five thousand pounds as a dowry, I would be able to attract you.'

Clive stared at her in astonishment, and the look on his face set her laughing. Slowly he joined in, but he was soon serious again.

'I don't find it all that funny, Emily. I know I said I would do anything to put back the loan I borrowed, but I didn't mean you to take it literally.'

'I couldn't bear it if you went to prison. And that's what would happen if the company find out.'

'I still can't let you——'

'You must,' she cried. 'Please, Clive, it's the only way I can repay you for all the kindness and love you've shown to me. I haven't forgotten the way you looked after me when Daddy died.'

'I did no more for you than a brother would have done,' he said gravely. 'And that's how I see you, Emily—as my kid sister.' He reached out and caught her hand.

'Not such a kid as I thought. I can't imagine you as a married woman.'

'I won't be—except by name.'

He looked taken aback, then as realisation dawned, he flushed. 'Good lord, I hadn't even thought of that side of it. What sort of man can Adams be to want to tie himself to someone he doesn't love?'

'I've told you, it's a business contract for a couple of years.'

Clive's eyebrows met above his nose. He was similar in looks to Emily, though considerably taller. There was more obstinacy in the set of his jaw and less candour in his eyes, but looking at the two of them together it was easy to see the blood relationship between them. 'And how does Mr. Adams plan to organise his social life once the two years are up?'

'I asked him that myself, but he was rather noncommittal.'

'He doesn't have a permanent relationship with you in mind, does he?' Clive demanded.

Emily smiled. 'I don't think he even knows what I look like! He probably pays more attention to his secretary.'

'He'd better keep it that way. If he starts making a nuisance of himself, let me know at once.'

'Certainly,' she said demurely. 'I can see the headlines now. "Cousin rushes to defend girl bride from husband." Honestly, Clive, you talk as if I'm a child!'

'I guess you always will be to me.' Clive's frown was more pronounced. 'If only we weren't having our books audited so soon, I would have been able to put the money back before anyone found out I had borrowed it. You do believe I didn't steal it?' he asked, and then went on without waiting for her answer. 'If the bottom hadn't dropped out of the Stock Market I would have trebled that money in a fortnight. As it is, the shares I bought aren't even worth a quarter of what I paid for them.'

'I'll give you Luke's cheque the minute I get it.'

'I'll let you have the shares in return.'

'I don't want them.'

'Maybe not, but you're going to have them. You're paying a high price for them, Emily. Two years of your life is a lot to give up.'

'I would do much more than that if I had to.'

'I believe you would, Funny Face.'

Arm in arm they left the café, Emily so engrossed with Clive that she did not notice the limousine slowly moving along the street, nor Luke Adams' startled exclamation as he saw her.

'So that was the man Emily Lamb loves,' he thought sourly. 'I hope he isn't banking on sharing her time once she's married to me.'

'Did you say something, sir?' his chauffeur asked, hearing a sound from the back of the car.

'I was just thinking aloud,' Luke said shortly, and folded his arms across his chest. He still did not know whether or not he was doing the right thing in staying with Charles Harrick. Perhaps he should have left and taken his chance of eventually being able to persuade Gina to come away with him. Yet she always had Charles's ill health as her trump card, using it to frighten him into maintaining their discretion. Even yesterday, when he had seen her for an hour and pleaded with her not to let him go on with this farce of a marriage, she had insisted they were doing the only possible thing in the circumstances.

'Charles is getting worse, not better,' she had cried.

56

'Neither of us would sleep easy at night if we did anything to give him a fatal heart attack.'

'Then at least agree with me that it would be better if I went to work for Watson.'

'And play into Roger's hands? That's exactly what he wants you to do. Leave the company so that he can step into your shoes.'

'They're miles too big for him,' Luke had retorted.

'It wouldn't stop him from trying to walk in them!'

It was this knowledge, more than anything else, which had finally made Luke agree to go on with their plans, though the sight of Emily looking adoringly up at the man she loved had unexpectedly soured him. Still, from Friday week he was buying her time, and he would make damned sure she gave him all of it.

CHAPTER FIVE

Luke's large sports car ate up the miles to the Robertsons' house in Oxfordshire. For most of the journey Emily sat quiet, nervous of the weekend that lay ahead of her and even more nervous of the man beside her, who was driving with the quiet ferocity of a tiger. Something must have happened to annoy him, for he had barely spoken to her since he had collected her from the hostel.

'Have you been busy in the last few days?' she asked when she could no longer bear the silence.

'Not more so than usual.'

'Have you had some bad news, then?'

'Why do you ask?'

'Because you're driving in a cross-patch way.'

'In a what?' The car swerved and straightened immediately. 'What the hell sort of way is that?'

'Tense at the wheel and foot hard on the accelerator. You'd find it much more relaxing if you did sixty instead of eighty.'

Instantly he slackened speed. 'Don't you like going fast?'

'It wasn't the speed of the *car* I was thinking about, so much as the way you're burning *yourself* up!'

He chuckled and his hands—large but long-fingered—gripped the wheel less tautly. 'You have a fountain of astonishing similes, Emily. You wouldn't be related to Lamb the writer?'

She smiled and shook her head. 'Nor to Lady Caroline.'

'I didn't think you were any relation of *hers*!'

'I've always felt sorry for her,' Emily said. 'She didn't have a happy life.'

'Would you say your life has been happy?'

'It would be more to the point if you asked me that question in ten years' time.'

'Why?'

'Because I still have most of my life ahead of me. I wouldn't like to judge my happiness on what I've had so far.'

He grunted and they drove several miles without speaking, the car moving at a less ferocious pace.

'I saw you in the street the other day,' he said finally. 'You were with a man.'

Surprised, she turned her head and looked at him. 'It was Clive, the cousin I told you about.'

'The man for whom you are marrying me.' He made it a statement, not a question, and she did not answer him. 'If you don't want to go ahead with the marriage, Emily, you have only to say so.'

'Does that mean *you* have changed your mind?'

'No,' he said abruptly. 'I'm still prepared to go on with it.'

She longed for him to be more explicit as to his reasons, for she found it hard to believe that Charles had only made Luke his Managing Director on condition that he had a wife. It was the sort of thing that might have been done fifty years ago, but not in this day and age. Yet she could see no reason why Luke or Gina should have lied about it. Perhaps there were other business reasons that they did not wish to disclose. With a start she realised Luke was speaking to her again, and at her look of enquiry he repeated the question.

'I asked you to tell me something about yourself, Emily. I don't know anything beyond the fact that you went to the same school as Gina.'

'We only overlapped for a year,' she said. 'Gina was older than me, but we kept in touch.'

'Why? You're totally different.'

'I don't know why. At least I know why *I* kept in touch with Gina—because she was the most glamorous person ever to come into my life—but I've no idea why she bothered with *me*.'

'That shows what a poor judge of character you are,' he teased. 'Don't you know that everyone loves to have a sycophant kneeling at their feet?'

'I'm no sycophant,' she retorted. 'I know all Gina's faults.'

'Tell me them.'

'I wouldn't dream of talking about a friend.'

He grinned, but forbore to tell her that Gina had no such compunction. My pet lamb, Gina always called her, and he had the strange feeling that in saying this, Gina was not only doing Emily an injustice, but showing up her own lack of judgment. Emily might be a lamb by name, but she was certainly not one by nature. A wolf cub was nearer the mark.

'What have I said that's so funny?' she asked.

'Nothing.'

'Then why are you smiling? I notice you often do when you talk to me.'

He thought the comment over. 'I think you should be pleased by it. Not many women make me smile.'

She was still thinking about this when they drew up in the curved drive that fronted a small, beautifully proportioned Queen Anne house.

The Robertsons in the country were considerably nicer than the couple she had met at Gina's party, and Emily immediately felt at home with them. Her hostess herself showed her to her room, which was well appointed with a couple of the latest novels on her bedside table and a tiny bathroom of her own.

'My husband and I will be in the drawing-room when you're ready to come down,' Mrs. Robertson said. 'You and Luke are the only guests this weekend, so it's all rather informal.'

'I'll enjoy that much more,' Emily replied. 'I was dreading a dressed-up weekend.'

'It would have been if Gina had been here.' Mrs. Robertson turned abruptly, as if she had said more than she intended, and then with a smile went out.

Emily was not surprised by the remark, for Gina was so lovely that she usually excited antagonism among other

60

women. Yet oddly enough she herself had never been jealous of her. Perhaps because their social lives had never touched and because the things Gina considered amusing she found deadly boring. Yet as Luke's wife she would have to condition herself to the same life as her friend. It was a terrifying thought and she refused to think about it. She started to unpack. If Luke did not like the clothes she had bought with his money then he would have to do her shopping himself.

But looking at herself in the mirror before she went downstairs she found it hard to believe he would object to her appearance. Anticipating a cold country house, she had gone for warmth as well as style, and the ruby velvet dress had both. High-necked, with a tight bodice that came in to a pointed waist, and long tight-fitting sleeves, it was mediaeval in style and went well with her glossy black hair, which swung around her face in a page-boy bob. Excitement gave colour to her cheeks and heightened the creamy pallor of her skin, making her eyes glow like forest pools, grey and fathomless.

There was a rap at her door and she called, 'Come in,' her racing pulse telling her it was Luke even before she saw his tall, broad-shouldered figure dwarfing the doorway.

'I came to see if you were comfortable.'

'Very,' she said. 'It's a lovely room. Where is yours?'

'Next door.' There was a lazy glint in his eye. 'The Robertsons are nothing if not diplomatic!'

'It would have been more diplomatic to have put us on opposite sides of the house.'

'Surely not,' he protested. 'Stubbing one's toes along dark passageways in the middle of the night ...'

She knew he was teasing her, but she could not help the swift colour that flamed her face, and she turned abruptly to the dressing-table and made a pretence of searching for a handkerchief she did not need.

'You're very innocent, aren't you?' He was close behind her and his hands came out and pulled her back against him, forcing her to stare into the mirror and see them standing together. She looked like a miniature beside him and felt far smaller than the five feet she knew herself to be.

'I could put you in my pocket,' he said lightly, and released her. 'Come along, little lamb. You look as if you could do with a drink.'

His gentle tone set the pattern of his behaviour towards her for the rest of the evening, and it was a pattern followed by her host and hostess. In the village where she lived Emily was used to being regarded as the efficient Miss Lamb, who was part-time social secretary to some rich people in London and part-time social worker to the old people in the village. If anyone was in trouble, if an extra pair of hands was needed or advice sought, it was always to young Emily that everyone turned. Even the vicar thought she had a better understanding of his young parishioners than he did. It was only the village doctor who saw her as she really was; an intelligent and resourceful girl whose mind was still barely utilised. Yet here, among these rich and sophisticated people, she was regarded as a child. It was an attitude encouraged by her diminutiveness, and she wished wryly that she could add six more inches to her height and an extra stone to her weight.

She sighed and leaned back against the armchair, enjoying the warmth of the log fire and the pattern that the flames made upon the timber ceiling. Luke sat beside her, talking quietly to John Robertson. The firelight made his hair look more silver than blond and she had the feeling that she was seeing him as he would look like thirty years hence. Age would not diminish his stature nor lessen the breadth of his shoulders, though she hoped it might soften the determination of his chin and the hard line of his mouth. He looked like a man who had fought hard in order to achieve his ambitions, and who possibly had even greater ambitions to achieve. Yes, she mused, shifting her head to watch him more easily, he was a man who had not yet obtained what he wanted from life and he would not rest until he had done so. Without warning he turned his head and she found his eyes probing hers. Quickly she lowered her lids and pretended to be dozing.

'I think Emily has gone to sleep on us,' Claire Robertson whispered.

'No, I haven't,' Emily said clearly. 'I'm wide awake and thinking.'

'About the economic situation, no doubt,' Luke said dryly.

'How did you guess?'

'From your pained expression.' He was still teasing. 'Tell me what solutions you have for our rocking economy?'

Sitting up straight, her hands clasped on her lap, Emily proceeded to do so. Her audience could not hide their astonishment and, seeing it, she grew more reckless than she might otherwise have been, and put forward theories she would normally never have aired.

'Well, well,' John Robertson gasped when she finally stopped. 'If ever you want a job as an economist, let me know.'

'Did you go to university?' his wife asked.

'Yes. I was at York.' Emily waited for Luke to say something, but he remained silent and she hid her disappointment, admitting to herself that she had shown off mainly to surprise him and to make him see her as a woman and not a child.

'How about a nightcap before we go to bed?' her host asked, pouring out a couple of whiskies as he spoke.

'Not for me,' his wife said, and looked at Emily. 'What will you have?'

'A glass of milk,' Luke spoke before Emily could do so.

'Chocolate, actually,' Emily said in her gentlest tone, 'and a teething ring to bite on at the same time.' She looked at Luke. 'It will save me biting you!'

He burst out laughing and the Robertsons joined in.

'Would you really like some milk?' Mrs. Robertson asked.

Emily nodded and stood up. 'But I'll make it for myself. Please don't bother. I'm very handy in the kitchen.'

Mrs. Robertson waved her to do as she liked and Emily

left the warm sitting-room and crossed the hall to the kitchen. The couple who cared for the house had already retired to their cottage for the night, and she opened the refrigerator for milk and got some cocoa from the larder. She was pouring the milk into a cup when she became aware of being watched and looked up to see Luke leaning against the edge of the table.

'The Robertsons have gone to bed. They told me to say goodnight.'

'Thank you. Are you going too?'

'I'll wait for you.' He held open the door for her and followed her back into the sitting-room where he resumed his seat, his hands still clasped around a balloon glass of brandy. 'I hope you didn't mind me teasing you tonight, Emily?'

'I don't mind being teased some of the time.'

'And the rest of the time?'

'I like to be treated as an adult.'

'Since you're going to be my wife next Friday, I would have thought the admonition unjustified.'

'You give me the impression that you see me as a child,' she asserted.

'You look like one.'

Irritably she set her cup on the table and half turned to him. As she did so the side of her body was outlined in the firelight, the material across her bodice straining against her small pointed breasts.

'Not quite such a child,' he murmured as his eyes rested on them. 'The more I look at you, the more of a woman you become.'

'Don't patronise me,' she said angrily, and jumped up.

'Sit down and don't lose your temper.' Luke spoke quietly, but she sensed the command behind the words and did as he requested. 'Why didn't you tell me you had a degree in economics?' he asked unexpectedly.

'You didn't ask me.'

'I assumed you would tell me the most important aspects of your life.'

'You engaged me to be your wife for a couple of years, not to join your statistical department. I don't see what my degree has to do with our future.'

'Now you're treating *me* like a child. You know very well what I mean. Ever since I met you, you've pretended that you hibernated in a village and that you worked for Gina to earn pin money.'

'I've done no such thing! I made it very clear to you that I need to work in order to earn a living. Why else do you think I'm marrying you?'

'To get five thousand pounds to give to your cousin, though why the hell you should want to do that, I can't imagine!'

'I love Clive and I'm——' she hesitated, wishing she could be truthful, yet knowing Clive would be furious if she were.

'And you're hoping he will feel grateful enough to marry you if you set him up in his own business? Dash it all, you're not an innocent child. You have an economics degree and you're intelligent enough to know the facts of life. Why throw yourself away on someone who only loves you for what you give them and not for what you are?'

'You're doing your best to talk me out of marrying you,' she said. 'Is that what you want?'

'Of course not.'

She was warmed by the vehemence with which he spoke, though it faded as he added: 'If you cried off, I wouldn't bother looking for anyone else. I'd forget the whole thing and leave the company.'

She drew a deep breath. 'I find it hard to believe that Charles is so insistent on your being married.'

'It happens to be true,' he said shortly. 'But for heaven's sake don't talk to him about it.'

'I wouldn't dream of discussing our arrangement with anyone. Anyway, why should I do myself out of ten thousand pounds?'

'Five thousand,' he corrected. 'You won't get the other half until our marriage is annulled.'

'You needn't be afraid I'll try and stick to you!'

His mouth curved, though it was more of a sneer than a smile. 'What will you do with the second half of the money. —give that to poor cousin Clive, too?'

'That's my business.' She stood up again and this time he did not stop her, but instead came with her to the door.

'I'll come up with you,' he murmured, and put his hand under her elbow. She was intensely aware that everyone in the house had gone to sleep and that she was alone with this tall, overpowering man who could pick her up in one hand and snap her neck like a flower stem. 'I'm a vegetarian,' he murmured lazily. 'I don't eat little lambs.'

'One more crack about my name . . .'

'I only have another week in which to do it,' he said. 'Come Friday, you'll be Emily Adams.'

She repeated the name and, as she did so, became aware that the tender look had completely gone from his face, leaving it hard and ruthless, as though he were thinking of something unpleasant. 'I'm sure there are many women who would love to be Mrs. Luke Adams,' she said quickly, hoping to restore his good humour.

'What does it matter how many there are,' he said harshly, 'if it isn't the right one?'

She longed to ask him what he meant, but knew it was unwise to do so. Besides, she had sufficient intelligence to guess. He had obviously been in love and something had gone wrong. She had never believed he had reached the age of thirty-three without being in love, despite his assurances to the contrary. She wondered who the girl was and why she had not wanted him. She must be a rare person indeed to turn down Luke Adams. She herself would never do such a thing if she had the chance. She stumbled on the stairs and would have fallen had he not put out a hand to steady her. She gripped the banister, more to stop her hand from shaking than because she needed its support. What on earth had made her think such a thing? She hardly knew anything about Luke, and the little she did know, she despised. She had always been scathing of big business and those who

66

made their living from it, yet here she was allowing herself to be swayed by the magnetism of one of the City's most successful tycoons. Magnetism. She caught eagerly at the word. That was all it was, the magnetism of a virile personality; a charisma that had nothing to do with reality. Like a schoolgirl dreaming of Prince Charming she, Emily Lamb, had let herself be carried away by handsome blond looks and a powerful physique. But a relationship needed more than looks to make it meaningful, and it would be as well for her to remember this in the months to come.

They reached the top of the stairs and walked along the corridor to her bedroom.

'Goodnight, little lamb,' he said, and leaned down to kiss her brow. 'Be ready to come for a walk with me in the morning. I'll be banging on your door at nine-thirty if you aren't downstairs by then.'

'Yes, my lord,' she said, and quickly closed the door to shut off his retort.

True to his word, Luke was waiting impatiently in the hall when she came down soon after nine-thirty in the morning. 'I've finally met a punctual woman!' he exclaimed. 'I don't believe it.'

She grinned and preceded him into the dining-room, where chafing dishes were set out on an electric tray. Helping herself to kidneys and bacon, she began to eat.

'I'm glad you have a good appetite,' he said. 'I loathe women who pick at their food.'

'*I'd* probably pick, if I had a weight problem. But luckily I can eat what I like without getting fat. I wouldn't mind putting *on* a few pounds if I could.'

'You're fine as you are. Nicely curved in all the right places.' He eyed her up and down. 'Extremely nicely curved, if I may say so.'

'By all means,' she replied. 'I love compliments.' She set down her coffee cup. 'I'll fetch my coat and meet you outside.'

'With a good pair of walking shoes, if you possess any!'

She grinned and left him, rejoining him in the driveway

a few moments later.

'I hope you're good for three or four miles?' he asked as they set off.

'I'll outwalk you any day, Luke Adams.'

'Don't be so sure.'

'I live in the country, don't forget, and you're a city slicker!'

'You don't have much time for people who work in the City, do you?' he asked conversationally.

'Are you passing the time of day or leading with the chin?'

He stopped and looked at her squarely. 'Leading with the chin. Tell me what you have against the City.'

'It isn't the city so much as the system by which it works. It's too easy for certain people to make a lot of money.'

'Every country has its élite.' Luke helped her over a stile. 'Even Russia and China have a ruling class, though they'll never admit it. But they at least recognise that certain jobs and professions give people different kinds of status, and that those with the highest status become aware of it and act accordingly. That's why you had your cultural revolution in China, and, your professors and scientists had to do their stint in the fields or factory to make them remember that they're no better than an ordinary labourer.'

It was the most serious speech Emily had heard Luke make, and she forgot her embarrassment with him and the strangeness of their association and was able to reply to him as if he were one of her own contemporaries. She only agreed with part of what he had said, and as they continued to walk, she discussed this with him.

One hour became two and two merged into three before Luke looked at his watch and stopped so sharply that she knocked into him. He gripped her by the shoulder to steady her and then kept his arm there. 'It's one o'clock already. Heaven knows how long it will take us to get back.'

'What time is lunch?' Emily asked.

'It's a help-yourself affair. Claire's having people in to dinner tonight and lunch is just casual.'

68

'Then we needn't go back for it. I'm sure we can find somewhere round here to eat.'

Luke stared at the bare fields, looking so much at a loss that she giggled. 'You're definitely not a country boy! Come on, follow me.'

Despite the concentration with which she had been talking, she had noticed a farm some ten minutes earlier and had seen a couple of children watching them curiously. Children in a farmhouse meant home-made bread at the very least, and a couple of slices washed down with fresh farm milk and home-made butter was more than enough to allay any pangs of hunger. She quickened her pace, and scrambling over a stile, pointed triumphantly to a beautifully timbered house nestling in a dip at the far edge of the field.

'Do you always make your dreams come true?' Luke asked softly.

'I haven't had much time for dreaming. I've always been too busy.'

'You'll have plenty of time from now on, Emily Lamb, though I hope that your reality will be so pleasant that you won't want to waste time with dreams!'

'I hope so too,' she murmured and hurried ahead of him.

CHAPTER SIX

EMILY looked on her farmhouse lunch with Luke as the time when her attitude towards him underwent a subtle but definable change. From the moment she had accepted his businesslike proposal of marriage she had been aware of a vague regret that they had not met under normal circumstances, and had frequently wondered how their relationship might have developed had this been the case. But sipping bowls of fragrant home-made soup, followed by farmhouse cured ham and chunks of crusty home-made bread with sweet butter, she felt as though she was meeting him for the first time and—equally important—that he was seeing her for the first time too. In well cut tweeds, as impeccably tailored as all his suits but with a shabby quality that came from usage, he looked far more like a prosperous squire than the Managing Director of a vast investment company. He looked younger too, and this made her realise that he generally behaved far older than his age. No doubt it came from working with men who were usually twenty years his senior; being long in the tooth seemed a necessary quality before one could achieve acceptance from the Old Lady of Threadneedle Street. She had always been aware of his quick wit but not known it could be gentle and warm until he displayed it as such in front of the farmer and his wife who, watching the way he smiled at Emily, could be forgiven for believing them to be a genuinely loving couple.

'And when are you planning to get married?' Mrs. Hardcastle, the farmer's wife, asked.

'Next Friday.' Luke shot Emily a glance. 'I don't believe in long engagements.'

'Will you be living down here?'

Luke shook his head and explained that they were only staying there with friends. 'I live in a flat in town.'

'That isn't good for bringing up a family.' The farmer's

wife gave Emily an appraising look as though sizing up the chances this elfin, slim girl had of being the mother of the children of this strapping man. She must have come to a favourable conclusion, for she nodded her head vigorously. 'You should get yourself a place in the country. There are still reasonably priced cottages to be found if you don't mind spending a bit doing them up.'

'I already have a cottage,' Emily broke in, hoping to change the subject to the less embarrassing one of houses. 'It isn't far from Cambridge.'

'Then I expect you'll be making your home there once your marriage has settled down. It generally takes a year before it does.'

'You talk as if marriage were a wine,' Luke smiled.

'It is.' The farmer himself came into the conversation, intercepting an amused look from his wife as he did. 'Marriage is exactly like a wine. If it's a good one it will improve with age, and if it's a bad one it will go sour.'

'Yours will be a good one,' said Mrs. Hardcastle.

Luke gave her a devilish grin and caught hold of Emily's hand. 'How do you know?'

'Not because I'd dare to judge *you*, sir,' the woman replied. 'You are a type I don't understand and that's honest; but your young lady now is as clear as water, and with the same ability always to get to level ground. You couldn't fool *her*, and if she's willing to share her life with you ...'

Luke's chuckle went deep and Emily was intensely conscious of his nearness and of his hand still holding hers. She tried to release her fingers, but he did not loosen his grasp and, glancing into his face, she saw that though he was still chuckling, his eyes were serious.

Later, as they tramped back across the fields, he returned to the woman's comments.

'She's right about you, Emily. I would never have thought to describe you as water, yet that's exactly what you are.'

'A shallow babbling brook?'

'A still, cool river.' Aware that she was breathing fast, he

71

slowed his pace and tucked her arm through his. It was a gesture made, she told herself firmly, to help her over the heavy, muddy ground. Yet she was touched by his solicitude, for he had given her the impression of being more concerned with her own welfare than with that of others.

'Tell me about your cottage?' he said unexpectedly.

'It isn't a weekend retreat in a storybook village. I've lived there all my life and so have most of the people around me. It's a farming community and a poor one. That's why I elected to go back there and work.'

'Miss Do-gooder.'

'I look after old people,' she said, ignoring the sarcasm. 'Most of the young ones tend to get jobs in the big towns and leave their parents behind, and this eventually creates a problem. Because a person is old it doesn't mean you can stick them in a geriatric ward and forget them.'

'What else can one do?'

'Lots of things. Several rich landowners I know have paid to have cottages on their estates turned into hostels. Old people can live there in a room of their own yet know there's always someone to hand to look after them if they become ill.

'You?' he questioned.

'Plus another social worker.'

'It sounds a full-time job. How have you found time to work for Gina?'

'It's my spare time, and she pays very generously.'

'I suppose you're going to tell me you use the money you get from her to spread a little happiness among the old folk?'

She saw the mocking tilt of his mouth and was furiously angry. Her eyes grew dark and her small white teeth bit hard on her lower lip to hold back the furious torrent of words she wanted to unleash.

'You don't mean you *do*?' he said in astonishment. 'You really do give away the money you get from Gina?'

Still she did not speak and he gave her a little shake.

'What do you live on?'

72

'I have my salary from the local council,' she said in a small voice, and refused to look at him as they continued to walk.

'You're a fool, Emily Lamb,' he said, but there was no longer any sarcasm in his voice. 'I thought people like you died with the dodo.'

'Then you don't know much about social work. No one who does does it for the money. It's totally at variance with *your* philosophy, of course.'

He gave her a slight shake. 'I was wondering when you'd be getting back to me! It's been all of two hours since you were last on the attack.'

Surprise at his remark brought her to a halt. 'I've never attacked you!'

'Not with words perhaps, but I wish you could sometimes see the look in your eyes. You make it very plain that you're contemptuous of what I do, and that you consider my job a waste of time.'

'I'm marrying you so that you can keep your job,' she reminded him.

'You're marrying me because you want the money.'

Quickly she averted her head, but was aware of him watching her as if he were trying to fathom what was going on in her mind.

'Why are you so eager to help your cousin?' he asked quietly. 'You don't strike me as the sort of girl to wallow in unrequited love.'

'I've already told you that I don't love Clive—in the way you mean. But we grew up together and—and——'

'If you only felt cousinly affection you wouldn't be willing to sacrifice two years of your life in order to give him money for his business.'

'Why not? Two years isn't all that long.'

'It can be a lifetime if you suddenly fall in love and want to marry someone else.'

'I'll take that chance.' She dug her hands into the pockets of her trousers and wished she could tell Luke the truth. Yet to an outsider, Clive's action would be construed as stealing, and loyalty kept her silent.

'I hope you won't regret your decision,' Luke said softly.

'Why should I?' Determined to lighten the mood, she tilted her head up at him. 'What makes you think it's such a sacrifice to marry you? You're a very eligible bachelor.'

'Am I?'

She continued to stare at him. A watery sun still shone in the sky, and in its light, Luke's hair sparkled like silver gilt. Even the firm way he brushed it flat could not destroy its vibrancy. 'I'm sure it wasn't necessary to pay someone to marry you; lots of girls would have done it for nothing.'

'Would you?'

'If I loved you.'

'Then it's a pity I didn't spend some time exercising my charm on you,' he replied. 'I might have been able to save myself a lot of money.'

There was a dangerous edge to his teasing and she took a step away from him, aware that they were standing close together in a secluded copse, with no sight nor sound of any other human being.

'My heart is too well protected to be bowled over by charm,' she said with as much composure as she could muster. 'Anyway, we've already made our arrangements. City gents don't renege on business commitments!'

His eyes glinted. 'You're never at a loss for words, are you?'

'It's my only talent.'

'I'm sure you have many others.' He came a step closer, his head low so that she could see the shadowed lids that partly hid his eyes. At close range his mouth was more curved than she had realised, its lower lip fuller and softer. 'Many talents,' he repeated, and before she could guess what he was going to do, he pulled her against him and pressed his mouth upon hers. It was a quick hard kiss, but she was intensely aware of the warmth and strength of him. He lifted his mouth away from hers but still held her close. She refused to tilt her head up to look at him and stared resolutely at the corner of the white handkerchief showing in his breast pocket, which was on a level with her eyes. The ground beneath her feet moved, and with a gasp she felt herself being lifted in the air until her face was level with his.

'I could crush you in my hands,' he said, 'and you wouldn't stand a chance.'

'Don't show off your male strength,' she retorted, anxious not to let him know how conscious she was of it. 'My father used to say that though I was small, I was indestructible.'

He smiled and set her to the ground. 'I know exactly what your father meant.'

Catching hold of her hand, they resumed walking. He seemed completely to have forgotten that he had kissed her only a moment ago, and she wished she could forget it as easily. But though the touch of his mouth had been fleeting, the pressure of it still remained with her, and she ran her tongue over her lips hoping to eradicate it. More than ever she found it strange that he was willing to lose his freedom in order to retain his job as Managing Director of Charles's company, and even more strange was the knowledge that Charles could have made such a ridiculous stipulation, particularly since he himself had been fifty before he had married Gina.

'Why didn't you call Charles's bluff?' She hadn't realised she had spoken aloud until Luke stopped and looked at her.

'What bluff?'

'His stipulation that you had to get married before you accepted the job.'

'He wasn't bluffing,' Luke said hesitantly. 'And anyway, I didn't think it was worthwhile to take the chance.'

'Is Harrick Investment so important to you?'

He did not answer at once and she had the impression he was reluctant to answer at all, but finally he did so, though there was no expression in his voice. 'What I've asked you to do is very important to me, Emily. Very important indeed.'

They left the Robinsons early on Sunday evening. Before

75

accepting the weekend invitation Emily had made it a condition that she was back in London by seven o'clock, but
she did not tell Luke the reason until they were driving
through the suburbs, when she asked him to drop her at
Charing Cross station.

'What for?' he asked.

'I'm going to Cambridge.'

'You mean you're going home tonight?' he asked, slack-
ening speed.

'Yes. I have to start work in the morning. I've only been
able to spend so much time in town this week because I had
some leave due to me.'

'Why didn't you tell me you wanted to return home tonight? I wouldn't have come back by this route if I'd
known.'

'I didn't want to bother you. It takes no time at all by
train.'

'You're crazy,' he said, and set the car going faster.

She watched the houses flash past and then swivelled
round to him. 'I'd like to talk to you about my job. I meant
to do so before, but there—but there hasn't been much
time. I suppose that after we're married you will want me
to give it up?'

'You suppose right.'

'Don't you think it's a waste of my training?'

'Probably. But I need a full-time wife.'

'Only a temporary one,' she reminded him.

'But full-time during the temporary period.'

She sighed. 'I was hoping we could work something out.'

'You mean you were hoping you could talk me into
agreeing with you!'

'Now you're being sarcastic.'

'I learn fast, little lamb.'

She conceded the point but still persisted. 'I'm sure your
flat is extremely well run and that there won't be much for
me to do. Can't I at least work part-time?'

'Provided you can convince me it won't affect your other
duties.'

'I will only be able to convince you if you keep an open mind.'

'My mind—like my life—is as open as a book.'

'But some of the pages are stuck together!'

He laughed. 'Ask me anything you like, Emily. I'm not at all the secretive man you assume me to be.'

'I think you're very secretive.' She searched his face, safe in the knowledge that his eyes were fixed on the road. 'I mean, you're very attractive and obviously capable of finding a wife, yet when it came to it, you chose me.'

'I told you my marriage is a *force majeure*.'

He was unexpectedly curt and she knew he did not like the turn the conversation had taken. Because of this she abandoned it. Each time she had broached the subject he had become withdrawn and she was more than ever convinced that there was an unhappy love affair in his life which he was trying to forget. This reason alone could account for his deciding to make his marriage a strictly impersonal one. She glanced out of the window and saw they were speeding along a wide ringway road.

'You aren't driving me to Cambridge?' she asked in astonishment.

'That's exactly where I'm driving you. You didn't think I was going to put you on a train at night, did you?'

'I have travelled by night before.'

'Not as my fiancée you haven't.'

'Is it official, then?' she asked.

'I think we can make it so. I'll ring Charles in the morning and tell him that after a weekend in your company I've decided I can't live without you.'

Hurt by his light tone, though she did not have any justification to be, she said: 'Don't lay it on too thickly with Charles. He isn't a fool, you know. He's bound to guess you aren't the type to fall hopelessly in love with someone like me.'

He did not answer, but she saw his hands tighten on the wheel and knew an illogical desire to meet the woman who *had* made him fall hopelessly in love. But there was no point asking him. He had already made it clear he did not wish to confide in her. Somehow she could not imagine his confiding in anyone. Despite his friendliness and charm, he gave away little of himself. Even this weekend, when he had learned so much of her own background, he had not disclosed any of his. She folded her hands in her lap and made herself more comfortable.

'I'm glad you know when to give in without arguing,' he said. 'I was expecting you to open the door and jump out.'

'I'm not a fool,' she said matter-of-factly. 'I'm delighted you're driving me home, even though I think you're crazy to make such a long and unnecessary journey.'

He chuckled. 'You're the only lamb I know with a sting in its tail!' Against her will she smiled and he echoed it. 'You look very pretty when you smile. It makes me realise how serious you usually are.'

She did not answer, but the first part of his sentence remained in her mind long after the second part had gone. Did he really think she was pretty when she smiled, or was he merely being polite? She longed to know what he thought of her, but knew that to ask him would be to invite his teasing. Instead she turned to the subject of their wedding.

'When is it going to be? I know you said next Friday, but——'

'Twelve o'clock at Caxton Hall. We'll have to have a small luncheon for some of our friends.'

'Won't Gina be giving that for us?'

'Gina?' He frowned. 'What makes you say that?'

'Because she said she would. Don't you remember?'

He shook his head. 'Can't you talk her out of it?'

'I doubt it. After all, she feels responsible for our marriage. Anyway, I think she's looking forward to making the party.'

'Do you?' he asked in such an odd tone that she was not sure what he meant. But he did not elaborate and instead turned to the subject of their honeymoon. 'Our going away is a bit of a farce, but if we don't take a few days off it will look odd.'

'And things mustn't look odd, must they?'

'No,' he said shortly, 'but we needn't go through the pretence of a protracted honeymoon. I thought a few days in Paris would do the trick.'

'Perfectly,' she replied, and wondered why she should feel so disappointed. Perhaps it was because she had been looking forward to spending at least a fortnight alone with him. It would have been an ideal chance of getting to know him.

'What's wrong?' he asked.

'Nothing.'

'You're lying. Tell me the truth.'

Giving him full marks for perception, she decided to be frank. 'I was thinking how nice it would be if we get to know each other. After all, we'll be seeing a lot of each other for the next couple of years and it would make things easier if we—if we didn't feel like strangers.'

'I don't feel like a stranger to you, Emily. In fact, I feel as if I've known you a long time.' He shot her a quick glance before turning his attention to the road again. 'Is it part of your training to make people relax with you?'

'It's what a good social worker aims to do,' she said composedly, 'though I wasn't consciously doing it with you.'

'What about subconsciously?' he teased, and slowed the car down, as if wishing to concentrate more on what he was saying. 'This weekend you've kept harping on my giving up my freedom for the sake of a job, yet you're giving up yours too.'

'I have no regrets, Luke. I've already told you so.'

He sighed and the car gathered speed. In less than an hour they reached Little Manning and drew to a stop outside the whitewashed walls of the house where she had been born and had lived for most of her life.

'Will you stay for supper before you go back?' she asked nervously as she led the way up the flagstoned path to the front door. He grunted, and taking it as acquiescence she went in and switched on the lights. He loomed large in the small hall and she immediately saw her home through his eyes. Though she appreciated the few pieces of lovingly cared-for antiques, she wished that the furnishings were not quite so shabby nor the carpets on the polished floor quite so worn. But it was a home which had been lived in and loved in, and she gained comfort from this. Opening the door of the sitting-room, she went round switching on the lamps. In the warm glow the room looked friendly and inviting and Luke took off his suede car jacket and dumped it on an armchair.

'Help yourself to a drink.' She pointed to the sideboard. 'I'll go into the kitchen and see what I can find. I'm afraid it won't be much.'

She was rummaging in the refrigerator when she heard his step and looked up to see him watching her.

'I wondered if you needed any help,' he said at her look of enquiry, and came over to peer into the refrigerator. Because he towered over her he was easily able to see into its depths and he reached out and withdrew a golden crusted meat pie and a bowl of tomatoes. 'I thought you said you didn't have much food.'

'Mrs. Banister must have brought it in. Yes, she did,' Emily repeated, taking out an open-faced apple tart fragrant with honey and cloves. 'This tart is her speciality.' Aware of Luke's quizzical expression, she felt emboldened to explain that whenever she went away from the village she left a front door key at the post office, and that quite often some of the old people whom she looked after would leave her special titbits that they had made.

'No wonder you don't want to give up your job,' Luke commented a little later as they sat at the well scrubbed table and devoured the excellent meat pie. 'This is as good as I've ever tasted.'

'I'll make it for you when we're married.' She blushed the minute the words came out, but knew it was hopeless to pretend she had not said them. Besides, Luke looked rather pleased at the prospect.

'I can't remember the time when I had a home-cooked meal.'

'Don't you have a housekeeper?'

'Yes. But I seem to eat out all the time.'

'You've just had a weekend of home-cooked meals!'

'Not in my *own* home,' he retorted.

Once again his answer reminded her that she knew little about his background beyond the fact that he had been a don. It seemed a good opportunity to quiz him and she did so. For an instant she thought he was not going to respond, but the good food had put him in a mellow frame of mind and after an initial hesitation he started to talk about himself. His background was more unusual than she had envisaged. His father's family had been an intellectual one while his mother's had been a prosperous Midlands one. It was in the Midlands that he had spent his formative years, dividing his time between a highly expensive boarding school and his grandfather's textile factory, where he had loved to work during his holidays and where he had obtained a first-class knowledge of the industry. His mother's death when he was fourteen had decided his father to resume an academic life.

'He had worked for my grandfather from the time I was born,' Luke explained, 'but when my mother died he returned to Cambridge and remained there until his own death a year ago.'

'So you were both at Cambridge together?'

Luke nodded. 'He was disappointed when I elected to go into the City, but I think he guessed it was inevitable.'

'At least he was alive to see what a success you were.'

'Success?' Luke echoed, and all at once looked bitter, as if the word evoked unpleasant memories. 'If one equates success with money and business achievement, then I *have* been successful; but there are other ways of equating it too.'

'I know,' she said softly, 'but I wasn't sure that you did.'

He caught his breath. 'That was below the belt again, Emily.'

'I didn't mean to. But we were talking truthfully and I hadn't monitored my thoughts.'

'Don't ever monitor them with me.' Unexpectedly he leaned across the table, the better to see her face. 'You don't know how much I welcome your honesty. It's a rare commodity in the business world and even more rare among women.'

Embarrassed, she jumped up and busied herself at the stove, then led him into the sitting-room to have their coffee. As soon as he finished it he stood up.

'When are you coming to London again, Emily?'

'I suppose it will have to be Thursday. It won't be easy for me to leave my job at such short notice.'

'They won't object, will they?'

She shrugged. 'I have four weeks' holiday due me and I'll take it in lieu of giving them my notice. If I didn't have such a good record,' she added candidly, 'my name would be mud.'

'I'm sorry,' he said softly, and touched her cheek. 'Incidentally, I liked your choice of clothes for the weekend. Particularly the dark red dress you wore on Friday night. It had an old-fashioned look about it that suited you.'

She smiled, at the same time wishing he did not think of her as old-fashioned. Why couldn't he see her as a sophisticated young woman with an appearance as bright as he claimed her personality to be? Who wanted to be considered a demure miss in ruby velvet?

'You aren't the Mata Hari type, Emily.' He spoke again, divining her thoughts with hurtful accuracy. 'You would look ridiculous in slinky black satin.'

'I'll surprise you yet,' she quipped.

'I don't doubt it.'

Allowing him to have the last word, she saw him to the door and watched until the tail lights of his car disappeared in the darkness. The weekend with Luke had given her a better understanding of him, and though she knew there were many facets she did not know, she no longer felt as if she would be marrying a stranger.

CHAPTER SEVEN

IT was a bleak November day when Emily became Luke's wife and, signing her own name for the last time, left Caxton Hall as Emily Adams. Charles and Gina were their only witnesses, but when they returned to the Harrick home the drawing-room was full of people, all of whom Luke appeared to know well. There was much joyful back-slapping and teasing and Emily wished she had not let her fear of Luke's sarcasm prevent her from inviting Clive. Sooner or later the two men would meet, but she had not felt that this was the most auspicious moment.

Yet momentarily alone beside the buffet, watching every-one laughing and drinking around her, she wished she had not been so logical and at least had one member of her family with her on this momentous day. For a momentous day it certainly was. Even a marriage entered into for busi-ness reasons had a solemnity about it that coloured the most bleak of reasons. She sipped her champagne and saw a slim young man coming towards her. She had been introduced to him already but could not remember his name.

'I'm Roger Harrick,' he said. 'Charles's nephew.'

'Gina has spoken of you.'

'I'll bet!' There was an inflection in his voice that in-ferred a deeper meaning behind his words, but he did not elaborate and she decided not to question him.

'Where are you going for your honeymoon?' he asked. 'Or is it a secret?'

'It's no secret. We're going to Paris.'

'City of lovers.'

There was a sneer in his voice and this time it aroused her irritation. For the first time she looked at him closely. It was easy to see his resemblance to his uncle, for he had the same light brown eyes and fawn brown hair. But he was paler in complexion and too thin. It gave his face unexpected angles and lent sharpness to his jaw and nose. Yet she could not in all honesty say it was a face she disliked, for it held character and he had a fearless way of looking at you that spoke for truthfulness.

'Have you known Luke long?' He was speaking again and she gave him her attention.

'Not really. We met here, as a matter of fact. Gina introduced us.'

'How clever of her!"

'Clever?'

'For knowing what a suitable wife you would make for Luke.'

'Or for knowing what a suitable husband he would make for me,' she responded.

'Let's hope you'll be able to say the same this time next year.'

'I'm sure I will—if I still know you by then.'

'I work at Harricks, Mrs. Adams. You're bound to see me frequently.'

'Not unless you learn not to make snide remarks.'

Momentarily he seemed disconcerted by her attack; then he smiled. It made him look disarmingly young and she had the feeling that nerves were making him sharper than he really was.

'Are you married?' she asked.

'Not yet. But you're running true to form by asking me.'

'True to form? I'm afraid I don't follow you.'

He smiled. 'All brides like to try and marry off everyone around them.'

'Perhaps we want everyone to be as happy as we are,' she countered.

'Are you happy?' he asked.

'Of course.' His look was so intent that she had the uncomfortable sensation that he was reading her mind. 'I think I'm very lucky to be married to Luke. He's the sort of man a girl dreams about.'

'Is he the man *you* dreamed about?'

'If he weren't, I wouldn't be his wife, would I?'

'I'm not so sure. There are many reasons for getting married, and love can often be the last of them.'

'Really, Mr. Harrick,' Emily said angrily, 'I find your humour in extremely poor taste!'

'I was not being funny, Mrs. Adams.' He moved in front of her, blocking her from the rest of the room. 'I know I can answer for the way Luke feels, but I must admit that *you* are a puzzle to me. If I didn't know better, I'd say you were genuinely in love with him.'

'There you are, Roger.' Charles Harrick had come upon them without being seen. 'James wants a word with you.'

With another questioning look in Emily's direction, Roger moved away and Charles took his place, content to stand beside her without talking. Emily was glad of his silence, for she would have found it impossible to make coherent conversation, so bewildered was she by Roger Harrick's last words. Instinctively she had rejected them, but like water on chalk soil they had permeated her being, and in doing so had crumbled her strength and immunity.

She was in love with him.

What a fool she had been not to recognise where her feelings were leading her; that she, who prized herself on her logical mind and matter-of-fact attitude, had not known what was happening to her. Yet she had had no prior knowledge on which to base her judgment. Even in her daydreams of a Prince Charming she had never considered herself beautiful or bright enough to capture a man like Luke. It was only a quirk of fate that had brought them together and her foolish heart had gone out to him without her being aware of it. She sighed heavily. No matter how much she had deluded herself about her own feelings in the past few weeks, she was not going to delude herself about Luke's. She might have fallen hopelessly in love with him but she knew that he still saw her as the same person he had met a fortnight ago. Little Emily Lamb who could get him out of a difficult situation: whose agreement to become his temporary wife would enable him to further his career and ambition, and who would, when the time was ripe, fade from his life as quickly as she had come into it. If only she had known where her emotions would take her she would never have agreed to Gina's suggestion. She would have picked up her skirts and run for her life. But it was too late to run now; it had been too late since the weekend she and Luke had spent with the Robertsons.

'I've never seen Luke so relaxed.' Charles Herrick interrupted her reverie and she forced herself back to the present. 'I think you'll be good for him, my dear. He needs a wife and a proper home; somewhere where he can relax and be himself.'

'Isn't he always?' she countered.

'Not Luke. He wears a mask that few people can penetrate. But then I'm sure you know that for yourself.'

'I don't know all that much about him,' she said candidly. 'After all, I've only known him a few weeks.'

'You know him well enough to marry him,' Charles smiled. 'And you aren't a little girl, Emily, you're a wife—at least you will be very soon.'

Warmth flooded her body at the implication of his words, but she refused to let it deter her from replying. 'Were you surprised when he—when Luke told you he was going to marry me?'

Charles rubbed the side of his face, the gesture reminding her of his nephew whom she could see watching her several yards away. 'Luke has always given the impression of being self-sufficient, too much so sometimes. For that reason alone, one can say one was surprised.'

'Can one be too self-sufficient? I would have thought it an ideal asset in the business world.'

'It is the rare person who has no chink in their armour, and I'm delighted that you are the girl who has found Luke's.'

Emily's eyes strayed to her husband. Her husband. It was the first time she had thought of him as such, but it was true. Regardless of how false their marriage was he was still her husband. Standing beside him in the registry office this morning listening to the words of the marriage ceremony, she had been infinitely moved by them, and she wondered now if Luke had given them any thought or if he had closed his mind to them, seeing them only as the small, unreadable print in a contract. For that was all their marriage was to him: a contract. Her hands clenched at her side. Her new-found love for Luke was awakening all sorts of foolish notions, not least of which was the hope that he might one day fall in love with her. On his own admission he thought she was beautiful when she smiled and she certainly had the ability to hold his attention and amuse him. As far as a relationship between a man and a woman went, it was as good as any to begin with and better than most.

'If Luke makes you unhappy,' Charles said softly, 'you can always come to me for help. Sometimes he can be tense and withdrawn, and you are so young and vulnerable.'

'Not so young and vulnerable that it's stopped me from earning my own living for the past two years,' she replied.

'You mustn't be a Mrs. Grundy about Luke's money,' Charles warned. 'I know you have a social conscience, but don't let it stop you from enjoying your life.'

'I can't see myself being idle.'

'I'm sure you won't be. I hope there will be children to keep you busy.'

The words brought such a vivid picture to her mind that she could almost see silver-blonde toddlers racing on a green lawn. She shut her eyes and opened them again to force the image away. But Charles was not to be dissuaded from it and went on:

'I'm looking forward to being a godfather to the first one, my dear.'

'Give me time,' she said huskily. 'I've only been married an hour!'

'Don't wait too long. That's the mistake I made.' His eyes grew pensive and she knew he was no longer in the room but somewhere back in the past. 'Gina was so young when I married her that I didn't wish to saddle her with children. I thought that if we waited a few years she would find the responsibility less irksome. But by then, of course, it was too late. I realised how ill I was and I didn't consider it reasonable to father children that I might not live long enough to help bring up.'

There were many answers Emily could have made to this, but since none of them could change the situation, she kept her peace. To tell Charles that she thought he had made the wrong decision or that Gina had been selfish in not changing his mind, would have served no purpose other than to hurt him or give him more regrets. So she murmured something unintelligible and made herself look sympathetic. Gina had never evinced much regret at not being a mother, had never mentioned her childlessness in fact, and Emily could not see her in a maternal role. She looked for her around the room and found her talking to Luke. They made a striking couple, both tall and with unusual colouring: Luke silver-fair, his skin tanned, his eyes Norse blue, his strong frame and broad shoulders making him look as if he would be more at home on the bow of a Viking ship than in a Mayfair drawing-room. And Gina, five foot eight of slenderness and grace; her eyes no less blue than his, her red-gold hair seeming to radiate its own light. From a distance she looked as young as Emily, and even at close range Emily knew she would not show her thirty years. But then the Ginas of this world rarely did. They were so involved in their own affairs that outside troubles did not impinge on them. Even the problems they might encounter always seemed in some magical way to be taken care of by other people. Yes, Gina was truly Sunday's child.

'I'm glad you'll be living in London, Emily,' Charles spoke beside her. 'It means you will always be here if Gina needs you.'

'I have been, anyway.'

'But you'll be closer to each other now that you are married; mentally closer, I mean. It isn't easy for Gina, you know. Her gaiety is an act. There are many times when I sense her despair, the anger and bitterness that is inside her.'

'Bitterness?' Emily echoed.

'That she can only count our future in months; that we're both afraid to look too far ahead.'

'But you're so much better,' Emily burst out. 'You haven't had a heart attack for a year.'

'Not a noticeable one,' he murmured, 'but several minor ones, and—and each time they do a little more damage.'

Her eyes filled with tears and she put her hand on his arm. It was difficult to think of Charles, so tall and straight, so young-looking despite his sixty years, as being so ill that he was afraid to look beyond tomorrow. 'I will always be here if Gina needs me,' she promised, 'but I'm sure you will be together for a long time.'

'Dear Emily,' Charles said and patted her hand. 'Come, let me introduce you to some of the other people. I've taken up too much of your time.'

She moved around the room with him, aware all the while of Luke doing the same. It was incredible how conscious she was of his every movement and she hoped with all her heart that she was not giving her feelings away. How horrified he would be if he knew. Yet surely it would not take him long to guess? She had never been any good at hiding her emotions, had never seen the need for pretence. If she liked someone, they knew it; and if she did not like them, they knew that too. But she must not let this happen with Luke. She had entered into a contract with him and he would not want the details of it to change. Yet this was what she was planning to do. Instead of being a temporary wife, she wanted to be a real one. The knowledge made her smile. How astonished everyone in this room would be if they could read her mind. They saw her as a happy young bride, not as a girl plotting ways and means of making her husband love her.

She glanced at her wrist-watch. She and Luke were catching the three o'clock plane for Paris and if they did not want to miss it they must soon leave for the airport. She looked round for him, but he was nowhere in sight, and deciding he had gone to collect his coat and make arrangements for the car, she decided to go to Gina's room to

89

collect her own things. Quietly she slipped out and ran up the stairs. She sped along the carpeted corridor. The sound of laughter from the drawing-room could no longer be heard and all was quiet, with a heavy silence that seemed to be at one with the damask walls and gilt candelabra. She reached Gina's bedroom and, opening the door, ran in.

The man and woman clasped closely together did not have time to draw back, but lifting their heads at the intrusion, remained locked in intimacy as they stared at her. Luke was the first to regain command of himself, and dropping his arms from Gina's body, stepped back and looked at Emily. But even he lost command at the sight of her pale face and flashing eyes.

The silence lengthened and Emily went on staring at Gina and Luke as if she had not seen them before. 'Yet I never have seen them before,' she thought dully. 'All I've done is to see my own image of them; my stupid, naïve image.' She went on looking at them and then with jerky movements, like a film that was being shown at the wrong speed, she crossed to the bed and picked up her coat. The mink coat Luke had given to her at Caxton Hall.

'A surprise for you,' he had said as he had dropped it over her shoulders. And now he had given her another surprise: a horrifying one.

In silence she went to the door, but before she could reach it Gina was standing in front of her, barring her from leaving.

'Emily—let me explain.'

'It isn't necessary.'

'It is. You don't know.'

'Of course I know!' Emily cried. 'I'm not quite such a fool as I look. I know exactly what game you're playing. Exactly why you wanted Luke to marry me. How could you?' she choked. 'How could you?'

'Emily, please,' Gina came close but did not touch her. 'You've got to listen to us.'

The word 'us' implicitly brought Luke into the manoeuvre. This was more than Emily could take and she backed away. 'You don't need to explain,' she retorted. 'It's all too obvious. Charles was beginning to suspect you and Luke and—and bringing me in as a wife was a marvellous ploy.' She swung round and gave Luke a derisive glance. 'I don't know who thought of the idea, but it's worthy of a medal!'

'We didn't do it because Charles is suspicious,' Gina said quickly. 'He has no idea that Luke and I—that we love each other. He regards Luke as his friend and the man who will be taking over his company. It was because Roger found out that we had to...' Her voice rose. 'Surely you see that we had no choice?'

'Of course I see it,' Emily snapped. 'It would have sent your world crashing down around your head if anyone had found out you were a faithless wife. And it wouldn't have done Luke much good either. The man who made love to the Chairman's wife in order to get to the top!'

'You know that isn't true!' Gina cried. 'You've no right to——'

'Let me handle this, Gina.' Luke had regained his equilibrium and the discomfiture had gone from his face, leaving it implacable as he looked at Emily. 'I can appreciate how you feel—finding me with Gina wasn't the most diplomatic way of letting you know the truth—and I'm sorry it had to happen like this and at this particular moment. I was going to tell you myself, but I intended to pick my time.'

'Oh yes,' she said bitterly.

'Yes, I was. Not that there was any need for me to discuss my private affairs with you.' His voice was unexpectedly hard. 'Our marriage is a business commitment—something we entered into with our eyes wide open. My being in love with another woman doesn't alter the situation *or* the reason why you agreed to marry me.'

'Of course it alters it,' Emily said furiously. 'I would never have agreed to marry you if I'd known you were in love with Gina.'

'Why?'

'Because I——' she clenched her hands and turned away,

91

knowing it was impossible for her to say what was in her mind. 'It's the deceit,' she continued slowly. 'I suppose people do get married for business reasons: diplomats, doctors or ministers maybe; but you wanted marriage so that you could continue to live with another man's wife.'

'Do you think Gina and I want it to be this way?' Luke grated.

'Then why maintain the secrecy?'

'Because of Charles.' Gina spoke again. 'If he knew the truth it would kill him. The shock . . .'

She did not go on and Emily nodded, understanding very well all that had been implied. How clear it all was; the reason for a marriage and the reason why she had been chosen. Little Emily Lamb was desperate for money; Gina's devoted friend; still at her beck and call, still foolishly seeing her as the kindly head girl at school and not as the faintly patronising benefactress of the present day. And what a benefactress! Bestowing her lover on Emily until such time as she was free to take him back.

'Learning that Gina and I love each other doesn't affect our bargain,' Luke continued. 'My marriage is still necessary.'

'And you're still being paid for it,' Gina added. 'Don't forget how desperately you want the money.'

Gina's words were a triumph of diplomacy, reminding Emily that her own reason for the marriage had been as pressing as that of Gina's and Luke's. Yet her reason had not been a deceitful one. As the thought came into her head she knew it was untrue. Clive had stolen the money from his company and she was abetting him in the crime, just as her marriage to Luke was abetting his love for another man's wife. She glanced at Luke and Gina, knowing derisively that none of them came well out of the situation.

'I'll wait for you downstairs, Luke,' she said. 'But don't make your goodbyes too protracted!'

Without looking at them again she hurried out, and only as she reached the end of the corridor did she stop and lean against the wall to try and still the trembling of her body.

How cruel Fate was! If she had learned about Gina and Luke a few hours ago it might have prevented her from ever coming to an awareness of her own love for him. But an emotion once discovered could not be forgotten, and no more was she the heart-free girl dreaming of a happy future. From now on her future lay with a cold, detached man: a man capable of living a lie, of being Charles's friend yet loving Charles's wife. It was this that horrified her more than anything, and though she tried to see it from Luke's point of view, she found it impossible. She appreciated that Charles's ill health prevented Gina from leaving him, but was nauseated by the way in which Gina and Luke were trying to get the best of both worlds.

The sound of laughter wafted up to her from the drawing-room and she moved away from the wall and walked down the stairs. She had reached the bottom step when Roger Harrick came into the hall, and after one look at her face he came forward and propelled her into Charles's study.

'Sit down,' he said, and as she obeyed, he went to the sideboard and returned with a tumbler of whisky. 'Drink it all,' he advised. 'It will make you feel better.'

Again she obeyed him, but as she went to put the glass down her hand shook so much that some of the whisky slopped over the side, and he took the glass from her without removing his gaze.

'What's wrong, Mrs. Adams?'

'I've just . . .' Emily caught her breath. 'I've just realised the meaning of your earlier innuendoes.'

'I see.' Instead of looking triumphant he looked discomfited. 'You really didn't know before, did you?'

'Do you think I would have married Luke if I had?'

He looked even more discomfited. 'I never believed Luke's story about love at first sight. I suspected from the start that he was getting married in order to keep me quiet, and I assumed he had put you in the picture.'

'Well, he didn't.'

'I'm sorry, I had no idea you were genuinely in love with him.'

'I'm not in love with him,' she said harshly. 'I'm—I'm just disgusted by the deceit.'

Roger pulled at his lower lip. It was the same gesture Charles Harrick made, and it reminded Emily of the man who was being so badly deceived.

'You are as guilty as Gina and Luke,' she cried. 'You forced them to take this step.'

'Hang on,' he protested. 'I never encouraged Luke to do anything. I said he must either give up Gina or leave the company.'

'You also said he could remain with the company if he married someone else.'

'I didn't mean it in quite those terms. I meant it would be all right if he fell in love with another girl. I never dreamed he would cook up a completely phoney marriage.'

Emily stood up, holding on to her coat to stop it slipping from her shoulders. The fur was silky against her neck and smelled faintly of her own perfume.

'I'd better go back to the drawing-room. It's getting late.'

'Of course. I'll——' He stopped as the door opened and his uncle came in.

'There you are,' Charles exclaimed to Emily. 'Luke has been looking everywhere for you. You must hurry if you don't want to miss your plane.'

Moving like an automaton, Emily made her goodbyes to the well-wishing guests and then followed Luke to their car. She must have acted the blushing bride well, since no one noticed anything amiss in her actions or appearance, and she was even able to suffer Gina's embrace at the front door.

'I'll talk to you when you get back,' Gina whispered. 'Please, Emily, try and understand.'

Emily could not bring herself to reply and she entered the car in silence. Luke did not break it until they were well past London and speeding to the airport.

'We'll have to talk this out, Emily.' His voice was brusque and formal. 'We're going to be alone together in

94

Paris for several days and we can either have a reasonably enjoyable time or turn it into a nightmare.'

'Perhaps it would be better if we didn't go.'

'Getting married so quickly was enough of a surprise to my friends without also doing away with the honeymoon. I intend to carry on with all our arrangements. Arrangements,' he added, 'for which you have already been paid.'

She thought of the banker's draft for five thousand pounds which had been sent to her yesterday afternoon and which she had immediately given to Clive, who had driven to the hostel to see her that night.

'You'll never know how grateful I am to you for doing this,' he had said. 'I'll never be such a fool again. If I want to buy shares in future, I'll do it with my own money or not at all.' He had put the draft away. 'You won't tell Luke Adams about this, will you? I work in the City and if this got out . . .'

'I won't tell anyone,' she had assured him, and had found his overwhelming relief faintly irritating. Deceit was a characteristic she loathed, but now she had married a man who was a past master in its practice.

She swung round to look at him. 'I'm not setting myself up as your judge. Only I would have thought more highly of you and Gina if you'd told me the truth.'

'I did tell you the truth. I needed to get married for business reasons, and that still applies.'

'You're playing with words, Luke.' He did not respond to this and her anger rose. 'Wouldn't it have been more honest to have given Gina up?'

'Roger wouldn't have been satisfied with that alone. If I wanted to stay with Harrick I had to get married to someone else. It was either that or leaving completely. I don't know whether or not you've followed the fortunes of Harrick, but since I joined them their profits have doubled—and that's not counting inflation! If I could find any way of remaining with them, I felt I had to take it.'

Though Emily tried not to be swayed by what he said, she could not prevent herself, and as her anger abated it was replaced by the deep anguish of knowing she loved a man who only had eyes for another woman. Bitterly she recalled her hopes of trying to make Luke fall in love with her once she was his wife. It was one thing to believe she could fight a past love and an unknown woman, but quite another to find that the woman was Gina and that far from being a past love, Luke's feelings for her were pulsatingly alive and in the present.

'Well, Emily,' he said. 'Can you understand why I did it?'

'Indeed I can. In many companies, promotion only comes by stepping into a dead man's shoes, and it's exactly the same at Harrick Investments. Except that when you step into Charles's shoes you'll also be able to step into his bed!'

'My God,' Luke said quietly, 'you do know how to hurt, don't you?'

'Can you think of any other way of putting it?'

He turned on her so sharply that she shrank back, afraid for an instant that he was going to hit her, but then he relaxed, his wide shoulders lowering. 'I know you like to call a spade a spade, but for heaven's sake try not to call it a bloody shovel.'

'What is that supposed to mean?'

'That sometimes even the bluntest words can't begin to approximate the truth. You have obviously never been in love in your life, so you don't know what it can do to you. If you had even a glimmer of an idea you would be more understanding.' He sighed. 'I suggest that from now on we don't talk about what happened. I'm willing to do my best to make our marriage work as smoothly as possible, providing you play your part.'

'I'll do what you've paid me to do,' she said, and would have given every penny she possessed to have been able to buy back her heart. But she had given it to this bleak-faced stranger. For Luke *was* a stranger. His understanding of loyalty differed totally from hers; his ability to simulate was so brilliant that she felt she could live with him for ever and never see beneath the charade to the man.

'Yes, Luke,' she reiterated, 'I'll fulfil my side of the bargain, but I'll be counting the days until it's over and we can say goodbye.'

'So will I,' he said icily. 'Let's leave it at that.'

CHAPTER EIGHT

EMILY did not expect to enjoy her stay in Paris, but to her surprise she loved every moment of it.

It was evening when they arrived at the Plaza Athenée, one of the most elegant hotels in the city, and were shown to the beautiful suite of rooms reserved for them. Luke spoke faultless French, which made her own attempts to do so sound hopelessly schoolgirlish. Not that it stopped her from speaking, and she rattled away to the chambermaid who came to turn down her bed. But it was only when she went into the sitting-room that divided her bedroom from Luke's that she realised he had overheard her, for he was openly grinning.

'I don't know who deserves the medal,' he said. 'You for having the gall to speak French or the chambermaid for being able to understand it!'

She smiled. 'Faint heart never won fair lady.'

'A faint heart could never win you.' Realising what he had said, he looked embarrassed, a fact which Emily noted with satisfaction.

'Where are we going for dinner?' she asked.

'Maxim's.'

'We're certainly playing the part well,' she retorted. 'A suite at the Plaza and dinner at one of the best restaurants in the country.'

'We won't be playing the complete part,' he said softly, and his narrow-eyed look made it impossible to deny the meaning of his words nor to see that he had said them deliberately to discomfit her.

'The only way we can make our bargain a success,' Emily said, taking the bull by the horns, 'is not to try to embarrass each other.'

'I didn't know you could be. You give the impression of being an emancipated young woman.'

'I *am* emancipated.'

'Have you had many lovers?' he asked easily.

'I haven't had any,' she replied, and then stopped, seeing his smile. 'The fact that I am emancipated,' she continued, in her haughtiest manner, 'doesn't mean I believe in free love.'

Smiling, he bridged the distance between them and came to stand in front of her. As always his tallness overwhelmed her and she backed away from him.

'Please, Luke, I can't bear it when you tower over me. It gives you an unfair advantage.'

'No advantage a man had over you could be considered unfair. You're such a spitfire that a mere male needs all the advantage he can get!'

She forced herself to smile, wondering what he would say if he knew he had a bigger advantage over her than any man had ever possessed before. Just to be near him turned her limbs to water and made a nonsense of all her confidently voiced independence. 'I am allowing his physical attraction to blind me to his character,' she thought fiercely. 'If he were ugly or weedy I wouldn't think about him at all.' Yet it was not merely his looks that attracted her but the sharpness of his mind and his gentle, teasing manner. But what about his deceit? a little voice inside her asked, and the question robbed the moment of all its pleasure.

'I'll change and be with you in half an hour,' she murmured, and went into her bedroom.

When she came out again she was once more in control of herself. Luke too appeared to have decided on a new plan of action, for he was attentive but courteous and treated her as if she were a young cousin to whom he was showing the sights of Paris for the first time.

That evening set the precedent for the days that followed, and they explored Montmartre, visited the Flea Market, drove to Versailles, went several times to the Louvre and the small galleries that were tucked into odd corners of the capital yet housed magnificent collections, and lunched or dined in the best restaurants that Paris had to offer.

Luke regarded France almost as his second home. During his years as a don he had spent his Long Vacations there and even after he had come to work in the City he had frequently flown to Paris for a weekend of what he saw as 'true civilisation'. But seeing Paris through Emily's innocent eyes he discovered its delights afresh. Her quick mind delighted him and he could not remember a time when he had been so amused and generally kept on his toes, as he was by this five-foot-nothing of a girl with a tongue longer than her body. And how furious she got when he teased her about her height. Laughingly saying one evening that he could put her in his pocket, she had rounded on him like a virago, causing him to make a mental note to be more careful in future. It was odd that she should want to be tall. As far as he was concerned she was just right. Occasionally when he sat across from her in a restaurant, he would think of Gina and the time when she would be able to sit opposite him instead, openly declaring their love for all the world to see. But as quick as the thought entered his head he would try to dismiss it, for Emily had sharp eyes and very little escaped her notice. Indeed he was surprised by his desire to monitor his thoughts in this way, and on the day before their departure he mentioned it to her.

'It's a good thing you're only five foot tall, Emily. As it is you make me quake when you fix me with one of your stares.'

'You aren't scared of anyone,' she commented.

'I'm scared of *you*. You have such high ideals that you make my conscience prickle!' She was instantly grave and he watched a variety of expressions fly across her face, though he could not analyse any of them. For a girl who could be so transparent she was remarkably adept at hiding her feelings, and he debated whether she had really come to terms with the way he and Gina had deceived her or whether she was only pretending in order to smooth the path of their temporary marriage.

'As it's our last day,' he said abruptly, 'I'll let you choose

100

what you want to do.'

'Have my hair cut. The best hairdresser in the world is in Paris.'

'Your hair looks fine to me.'

'That's because you don't really see me.'

'Of course I do.'

'Then close your eyes.'

'What for?'

'Close them,' she said, and as he did so, added: 'Now describe me.'

Luke was annoyed at having fallen into such a trap, but wryly conceded that he had been fair game. 'You're five feet tall, perhaps half an inch more, your skin is pale, your hair is dark and you have grey eyes.' He went to open his, but felt her fingers instantly on his lids.

'No, you don't,' she firmly said. 'I want a better description than that. How dark is dark, how pale is pale, and what *sort* of grey are my eyes?'

Carefully he allowed his inner eye to dwell on her, bringing to bear all his acumen, but he could not enlarge on the description he had already given and, taking his mind away from the first time he had seen her, moved his memory along to the time when he had first felt he was beginning to understand her: the weekend they had spent with the Robertsons. They had gone for a walk on the Saturday and had lunched at a farmhouse, where Emily had soon been giggling with the farmer's children. She had looked like a child herself as she had sat on the floor playing with the little girl. Her hair had gleamed like sealskin and her cheeks had been roses blooming into life. Keeping his lids shut tight, he spoke again.

'Your hair is like a tropical sky at night: gleaming black yet interspersed with points of light. You have the luminous skin of a Botticelli angel and your eyes are smoke. You have a baby-shaped mouth with a short upper lip that's extremely sexy and your figure is——' He stopped as her fingers abruptly ceased their pressing, and opening his eyes he stared straight into hers, or at least as much of them as

101

he could see beneath the veil of her lashes. Her eyes *were* like woodland smoke, he thought amusedly, though he had merely made up the simile in order to tease her; as indeed he had made up the whole description. Yet staring at her he saw that he must subconsciously have noticed her features and colouring, for she was exactly as he had described her.

'Do you want to know how I see *you*?' she asked.

'No, thanks. I'd rather like to keep some of my illusions!'

'I didn't think you had any.'

'A man with no illusions is a man without a soul. For what is a soul but a man's illusion of his omnipotence?'

She pulled a face at him. 'I refuse to have a serious discussion with you right now. We were supposed to be talking about my haircut.'

'No talking is necessary,' Luke smiled. 'You may have the whole day free, providing you meet me for lunch at the Tour d'Argent.'

'I won't need the whole day,' she replied. 'Just a couple of hours.'

'I'll double it and give you four. So meet me at the restaurant at one-thirty.'

'Another light lunch at twenty pounds a head,' she commented.

'Now you're talking like a wife,' he teased, and thought of this remark as, an hour later, he wandered along the Champs Elysées, wondering how to fill in his time. Somehow he could not think seriously at the moment. It was as if his mind were in limbo and his critical faculties held in abeyance. Only a feeling of pleasure and sensual aliveness was operative, which was the way it should be on one's honeymoon. If only this were a real honeymoon and he was with Gina. The thought of her was suddenly so unbearable that he plunged into the nearest café to use their telephone. Within a few moments Gina's voice came over the wires, husky and soft in his ear and making him throb with desire for her.

'I've been thinking of you the whole time,' she said, 'and

hating Emily for being with you when I can't.'

'How is Charles?' he asked, and was immediately horrified at the way his mind had worked.

'Very tired. He hasn't been to the office the last few days.'

'I'll be back tomorrow. I would have come back earlier if you'd let me know.'

'Don't be silly, darling. You're on your honeymoon, remember?'

'I wish I could forget it,' he said violently; a remark which seemed to please her, for she immediately sounded happier.

But Luke felt more unsatisfied when he finally put down the telephone. Hearing Gina's voice in no way appeased his longing for her, though it added to the burden of guilt he carried round with him. How little Emily knew of him if she thought his deceit rested lightly on his shoulders. What would she say if he told her of the hours when he had paced through the night wondering what to do? He frowned. He knew darned well what to do but he lacked the strength to carry it out. Once Roger had made his threats he should have left Harricks and never entered into this charade with Emily. His frown grew deeper. He must make a point of meeting her cousin when they returned home. What sort of man was it who could allow a girl to enter into such a commitment in order to provide him with the necessary capital to set up in business? He was still feeling contempt for this unknown cousin when he arrived at the Tour d'Argent and went up in the small lift to the restaurant that gave its clients one of the most beautiful views in Paris. He asked to be shown to his table and sat there, staring out at Paris far below him while he waited for Emily.

Time passed and he glanced impatiently at his watch. Like all her sex, Emily obviously lost all sense of time once she got into the hands of a hairdresser. A faint stir at the end of the room drew his attention. A young woman had come in and was talking to the head waiter. She drew the eyes of all the men, for she radiated beauty and vitality.

Short black hair curled round her head like osprey feathers, with several fronds curving forward on to her cheekbones and the hollows of her cheeks. More tendrils caressed the lobes of her ears but left her neck free to rise, white and slender, from the collar of a demure but figure-fitting suit in a subtle shade of tangerine. The colour gave a glow to the girl's startlingly beautiful complexion: she really had the skin of a pearl. The pert little head tilted in his direction and the tangerine figure came towards him. Swallowing his astonishment, Luke realised he had been staring at his own wife.

Even when she had sat down and ordered herself a drink, he could not take his eyes away from her. It was incredible that a haircut could make so much difference to her appearance. But it was more than a re-styling of her hair. She was wearing an outfit he had never seen before and different make-up from normal. Her eyelids were delicately shaded in some colour that gave her eyes a violet tinge and made them look twice as large as he remembered them; and he could only think she was wearing false eyelashes, so long and thick were they, though as he leaned across the table he saw they were her own. Funny that he had never noticed them before. She was wearing a different shade of lipstick too: it made her mouth look soft and moist, and he was reminded of Gina's mouth, and the feel and taste of it. Abruptly he caught hold of his thoughts.

'You look different,' he said lightly.

'Do I meet with your approval?'

'You know you do. No girl who can come across a restaurant with such poise needs to be told how lovely she looks.'

'I *am* pleased with myself,' she confessed. 'But I'm afraid it's cost you a fortune. I hope you don't mind?'

He laughed. 'I'm glad you have no false modesty about spending my money.'

'You can afford it,' she said calmly.

'Quite easily. So how about some champagne to celebrate the fact?'

She nodded. 'And also to celebrate our return to England and the new life ahead of us.'

Warily he looked at her but her expression was artless.

'Our stay in Paris has been a kind of curtain-raising,' she explained. 'A prologue to the play, as it were. But once we're in London, the play proper will begin.'

'And continue until the curtain comes down on the last act.'

'Of course; when Charles is dead. That will really be curtains for us then, won't it?' She smiled. 'Don't bother to deny it.'

'I wasn't going to.' He sensed rather than saw her flush and wished she were more realistic about Charles's ill health. Yet in the beginning, when he had first realised his love for Gina, he too had been sensitive about Charles. Stepping into a dead man's shoes. The words filtered into his mind and were savagely pushed out of it. Blast Emily for her sharp tongue! She should never have said such a thing to him.

'Let's order lunch,' he said with a calmness he did not feel, 'and the champagne, of course.'

Emily half smiled but remained quiet. Instinctively she felt that a change had come over him in the last few moments. She knew it was nothing she had said and wondered if their conversation had reminded him of something else. Deliberately she started to talk, giving him a witty account of her two hours at the hairdresser's and her two hours in the exclusive boutique attached to it. Soon Luke started to smile at her description and within a short time was laughing openly as she mimicked the effete young man who had re-styled her hair. She put up a hand to touch it, still unused to its shortness.

'Do you like it?' she asked.

'Very much. And your suit too.'

'I bought some other things as well,' she confessed. 'On our way back to the hotel I'd like to collect them. I was only able to pay for this suit. I had to leave a deposit on the rest.'

'How much will you want?'

She mentioned a sum which she considered to be astronomical but which did not even cause him to blink an eyelid.

'Luckily I have an account in Paris,' was his only comment. 'If you want to get anything else, there'll be no problem about it.'

'Things are very expensive here.'

'But smarter. Go out and buy whatever takes your fancy.'

'Will you come with me?'

'I have a few calls to make.' He hesitated. 'I thought I would put one in to Charles; he isn't well.'

Emily knew without being told that he had already spoken to Gina, and felt such a wave of dejection that it was all she could do to go on eating. She had still not overcome this feeling when they left the restaurant, though once she had said goodbye to Luke and set off to do her shopping, her spirits revived. If he ever realised how the thought of Gina spurred her to uncharacteristic extravagance, she thought as she recklessly bought one outfit after another in an exclusive little shop on the Faubourg St. Honoré, he would never mention her name again! Despite herself, the idea of this made her smile, and the vendeuse, assuming it to be satisfaction with her purchases, hopefully offered her yet more exclusive models.

'Madame is *très facile* to fit,' the vendeuse chirped. 'Not as tall as a model, but equally slender. Shortening a hem is easily done.'

Emily allowed herself to be talked into several more purchases, commanded them to be sent to her hotel and continued on her way. It was five o'clock when she returned exhausted to her suite, where she soaked for a long time in a bath and then rang for a maid to unpack the things she had bought and put them in the set of cream-coloured airweight luggage to which she had also treated herself.

'But please leave out the black chiffon,' she said. 'I want to wear it tonight.'

Emily had never considered herself a sybarite, but

emerging from the bathroom, warm and perfumed, to enter her rose-shaded bedroom and see the silk lingerie on the bed, the black dress floating on its hanger in the wardrobe and a white mink jacket lying nonchalantly across the back of a chair, she became aware how easy it was to succumb to luxury, and experienced a pang of guilt at the knowledge that the money spent on the fur alone would keep one of her old pensioners for a year. The realisation that she would not have spent such a vast amount on clothes had she not been angry with Luke for deceiving Charles only added spice to her actions; a spice that was heady enough to overcome her unhappiness.

Darn Luke and Gina! They had played her for a fool and now she was going to take advantage of the part they had created for her. She would not be playing it for long, so she might as well enjoy it while she could. But she must not allow herself to lose her social conscience. She pulled a face. How priggish the words sounded, and how derisive Luke would be if he heard them. Did he ever think of all the people less fortunate than himself or was he so wrapped up in the world of high finance that he had no time to spare for the hundreds of thousands whose daily, monotonous existence helped to build the pinnacle on which he sat? It was a question she would like to ask him, but she must pick her moment.

Pushing her own social conscience aside, she stepped into the black chiffon. The skirt sighed softly around her, falling wide from a tightly nipped-in waist. The bodice was tight too and the black silk lining barely reached the curve of her breasts, leaving the rest of her skin to be covered by the gossamer-fine chiffon. The sleeves were long and tight, fastened at the wrists by a row of tiny diamanté studs. Careful not to tear the fragile material, she went to zip up the back, but she could only reach her waist, for from then on it was fastened by buttons. She rang for a chambermaid, wishing she had had the foresight to tell the girl who had been doing her room to come back. While she waited for her call to be answered she finished her make-up and hair.

She liked the way it bounced with every movement of her head and its provocative curl upwards as it reached her ears. It made her face, which she had always considered to be round, look heart-shaped, and this in turn made her eyes appear larger. How shiny they were with excitement.

She stared at her mouth, wishing it was more voluptuous; a short upper lip made her look like a child. She was too used to it to realise how sexually provocative it was, though Luke, coming into her bedroom to see if she was ready, was immediately aware of it. He was also aware of how beautiful she looked. She would make some man a wonderful wife. With a shock he realised she was *his* wife, and he could not help experiencing a twinge of sadness that such loveliness was wasted. Emily should have married someone who loved her; someone who would care when her eyes shone at them and who would want to kiss that smiling, mischievous mouth. Not that he would object to kissing it himself, he thought idly, and because the thought was treacherous to Gina, he pushed it away.

'Sorry to barge in,' he apologised. 'I thought you would be ready.'

'I am. I'm just waiting for the maid to do up my dress.'

'May I help you?'

She hesitated and then obligingly turned her back on him. 'The buttons are very small,' she said in a subdued voice. He did not reply, but she felt his fingers warm on her skin as he began to fasten them. She tried not to be conscious of his nearness, but he was so close to her that the slightest movement on her part enabled her to feel his body.

'There,' he said, and there was a faint tremor in his voice.

She swung round. 'Will I do?'

'Do you need me to tell you?'

Her smiled flashed as she turned to pick up her jacket. The fur enhanced the pearly gleam of her skin and she looked like a chocolate box beauty: her face framed by white mink, her jet black hair gleaming like a raven's wing and her wide-apart grey eyes glowing like some exotic jewels.

'You're a very beautiful young woman, Mrs. Adams,' he said. 'As I'm sure you know.'

'A girl still likes to be told.'

He caught her arm and tucked it beneath his. 'I'm going to be the envy of every man who sees me tonight.'

'It's a good thing they don't know we're only pretending.'

In the act of walking with her to the door he stopped. 'Don't say that.'

'Why not? It's true.'

'It isn't. When I said how lovely you were I meant it. Every word. I just regret that—that this honeymoon can't be real for you.'

The flush on her cheeks deepened. Had Luke guessed she was in love with him? Surely not. She had been so careful not to give herself away.

'You should be married to a man who will love you and cherish you,' he continued. 'Not a man like me who can't give you anything except——'

'Five thousand pounds,' she interrupted, hoping he did not know the effort it cost her to say this. 'Dear Luke, how sweet and old-fashioned you are underneath your worldly air. Just because I'm five feet nothing and look like a child, don't think me an innocent. We both went into this marriage for our own reasons, and those still apply.'

'They shouldn't have applied for you,' he said abruptly.

'I don't want to talk about it.'

'Very well, Emily, I won't.'

For the rest of the evening Luke set himself out to entertain her, and Emily could almost believe she really was a bride on her honeymoon in Paris. If only this make-believe were true! She wondered what sort of lover he would make. Masterful, of course, there was no doubt of that, but tender too, and knowing when to sublimate passion to humour. Though he had only kissed her once, there had been nothing callow about it; his touch had been expert and she knew he would be skilful at rousing the response he wanted and patient until he had achieved it.

'You're staring at me with a very troubled look,' he interrupted her thoughts, and one eyebrow rose as he saw scarlet glow in her cheeks. 'Were they such terrible thoughts?' he went on.

'I was wondering what sort of lover you would make.'

He choked on his wine and set the glass quickly on the table. 'I doubt if you'll ever lose the habit of surprising me. You're shameless, Emily, do you know that?'

'Don't be silly.' Seeing brazenness as the best way of hiding her desire to throw herself into his arms, she went on: 'Anyway, I'd be surprised if you hadn't thought the same about me at one time or another. Even though you're in love with Gina,' she added recklessly, 'you aren't blind to other women.'

'I'm not blind to *you*,' he corrected.

'Fine feathers make fine birds.' She waved her hand deprecatingly and found it caught by his and held tightly.

'Don't underestimate yourself, Emily. I noticed you long before the fine feathers. You aren't a girl a man can ignore.'

'I'm not a beauty either.'

'Aren't you?' His eyes narrowed and the blue of them seemed to intensify. 'You're a bit like the nucleus of an atom—devastatingly explosive.'

'Not as destructive, I hope,' she laughed, and pulled her hand away from his.

'More so,' he replied, but did not elaborate and signalled to the waiter that they were ready for coffee. 'If you have no objection,' he said, 'I would like to catch an early plane tomorrow. I want to get back in time to see Charles.'

'For business or personal reasons?'

'What do you mean?'

'Don't you know?' she asked scornfully, hurt pride making her speak when she knew she should be silent. 'Do you want to see how ill Charles is because you care about his health or because you want to know how soon Gina will be free?'

'For heaven's sake!' he exploded. 'Don't you know when

to keep quiet?'

She stared down at the tablecloth, mortified to feel tears spilling down her cheeks.

'Don't cry,' he said roughly. 'That would be the last straw.'

'I'm sorry; you have every right to be angry with me.' She wiped the tears away and then forced herself to give him a brilliant smile. But tears still glimmered on her eyelashes and she looked heartbreakingly young and defenceless.

'Oh, Emily,' he whispered. 'I don't want to hurt you, and yet ... We should never have married. The whole thing was a mistake. You're a child. You aren't the type to act a part like this.'

'I think I've acted very well so far.' She was determined not to let him pity her. 'Just bear with me a bit longer and I promise I won't lose my temper at all.'

'Don't make a promise you'll never be able to keep!'

The humour was back in his voice and she relaxed, but there was still something she had to say and, clenching her hands beneath the table, she forced herself to speak. 'If anything *should* happen to Charles—I mean sooner than you expect—I'm quite prepared to—well, there won't be any problem about getting your freedom. I'll leave you any time you wish.'

'Thank you.'

'Luke, you old son of a gun!' A whisky-warm voice broke in on them, and Emily looked up to see a man in his middle forties.

He was accompanied by a woman and another couple. They were all elegantly dressed and had obviously dined well. They appeared to know Luke well and suggested he join them at the night club to which they were going. Luke glanced at Emily and, because she could not bear the thought of going back to the hotel and lying awake for most of the night, she nodded and said she'd love to go on somewhere else.

Emily had never been to a night club before; a discothèque was the nearest she had come to it, and it was a far cry from this dark, sophisticated interior where the music was soft and sensual and champagne seemed to be the only drink. The floor was surprisingly large and there was plenty of room to dance, so that she knew it was inevitable that Luke would take her in his arms. Because it was something she had looked forward to for so long, the moment came almost like an anticlimax, and she gave a sigh of relief as they glided away from the table. Luke's arms were around her and she knew no feeling of excitement or tension, merely a sense of coming home. He heard her faint sigh and pulled her closer.

'We needn't stay long if you're tired. But I thought you wanted to come.'

'I did. I love dancing.'

'Do you do much?'

'Not since I left university. There's only the weekly hop in the village and the local yokels are rather heavy on one's toes.'

'Beats me why you stuck yourself in a village. You should have lived in London. There are no shortage of jobs there.'

'I've already told you why I wouldn't leave. Too many of the young people moved away. I felt it my duty to stay.' She made a face. 'How priggish that sounds!'

'I don't see you as priggish. You're honest and you say what you feel.' He twirled her round and bent low over her as the tempo of the music changed and the insistent beat of bongo drums filled the air. The music quickened, grew faster still, and Luke stopped and shook his head. 'I'm out of my class, I'm afraid.' He went to lead her back to the table and a young man stepped in front of them, murmuring in French and smiling.

'You've made a conquest,' Luke said to Emily. 'Do I hit him on the jaw or——'

'I'll dance with him,' she said, and gave the young man such a wide smile that he forgot to say thank you to Luke.

For the next fifteen minutes Emily gave herself up to the

joy of dancing. She had rarely had the opportunity of doing so in the past few years, and she had forgotten the thrill of allowing her body to find its rhythm. But in this dim Paris night club that made London seem like years ago, she forgot the past and present and even the bleak future, and thought only of this exciting, pulsating moment. She was breathless when she finally returned to the table, declining her partner's offer to dance again.

'I hope you didn't mind my leaving you?' She fanned herself as she spoke to Luke.

'You taught me a lesson in African dancing,' he smiled. 'And made me realise we're a generation apart.'

'You aren't as old as that,' she protested.

'I feel it with you.' He glanced over her shoulder. 'Your dancing partner is still looking in your direction.'

'He's wasting his time,' she said. 'I would like to go back to the hotel; I'm tired.'

At once Luke stood up, and bidding goodnight to his friends, who seemed all set to see the night out at the club, they returned to their hotel. Ignoring the lift, they walked up the one flight to their suite. Emily's feet were hurting her and she took off her silver sandals and held them in her hands. Her chiffon skirts drifted around her as she swayed with tiredness.

'Poor baby,' Luke murmured and, swinging her up into his arms, carried her into their sitting-room, kicking the door shut behind them. Even here he did not set her down but strode across to her bedroom and dropped her on to the bed. She bounced gently and then lay back against the pillows.

'Thank you for a lovely evening,' she said, and held up her hands to him.

'I should be the one to thank *you*.' He caught her fingers and bent slightly forward. Unaware that he was going to do so, she raised herself to say goodnight to him and found her face almost touching his. Silently he pulled her forward until her mouth was touching his. Only then did he release her hands and, putting his arms around her, pulled her

113

against him. His hands were warm through the thin chiffon and she felt the pressure of his fingers as they moved across her back and down her spine.

Emily knew she should resist him, but it was impossible to do so. She was too emotionally overwrought and her hands came up behind his head and pulled him closer still. How soft his hair was, and how soft his lips. She shook with a wave of uncontrollable emotion, her limbs trembling as though with fever. He moved swiftly and she felt the weight of his body as he pressed her back against the coverlet. She opened her eyes and looked at him, but his face was too close for her to see it properly, and she was only aware of the dampness of his skin and his breath, quick and heavy on her cheek as his lips left hers and travelled down her shoulders to the curve of her breast. The delicate chiffon pulled and he started to undo the buttons behind her.

'Gina,' he whispered.

With a gasp Emily wrenched free of him. The violent movement tore her dress, but she was beyond caring. All she knew was that Luke had betrayed her. No, that wasn't true, she had betrayed herself. She had wanted him so much that she had forgotten Gina, but he, though roused by passion enough to lose his head, was still subconsciously holding the woman he really loved in his arms. His use of her name had proved this beyond all doubt.

'Please go.' Her voice was thick with tears but she hoped that if she kept it low he would not notice.

'Forgive me,' he murmured.

'It was my fault. Next time I'll remember that men have a low threshold of excitement!'

Abruptly he strode across to the door and did not look back as he closed it behind him.

CHAPTER NINE

IT was one thing to be Luke's wife on honeymoon in Paris and another to be his wife and share his home in London, where every room she entered and every object she touched brought him vividly to mind.

The days passed slowly, for without her social work time hung heavily on her hands. She had frequently envied Gina the life she led, but faced with it herself, she found it empty and boring.

Gina. The very name brought with it memories of her in Luke's arms, and Emily was honest enough to admit that this would now affect her entire relationship with a woman she had considered her friend for years. Yet had they really been friends? Schoolgirl infatuation might be a better description, for whatever it was that had existed between them, it existed no more. It was painful to admit that Gina had used her for her own ends, but it was undoubtedly true. Had there been a genuine bond between them, Gina would never have allowed her to marry Luke without telling her the true position. Now that her eyes were open, Emily saw many things she had been too blind to see before, and this was the most painful part of her new life as Mrs. Luke Adams: the knowledge that she had given her friendship to someone who had not merited it.

Within an hour of returning from Paris, Luke had gone to see Charles, but Emily had pleaded tiredness and had remained in the flat, using the time to unpack her clothes and turn the spare bedroom into her own. It had been late when Luke had come home and though she had enquired about Charles, she had deliberately refrained from mentioning Gina. She was sure Luke noticed the omission, for he deliberately brought Gina's name into the conversation and Emily, as deliberately, had ignored it. Charles, it seemed, had had another heart attack and had been advised

115

to take things easy for a month. But he was only buying time and he knew it, for he had insisted that Luke come to see him each day to talk over the affairs of the company.

'I shouldn't have thought there was much more Charles could teach you,' Emily had remarked.

'We don't talk about day-to-day events,' Luke had admitted. 'Charles likes to talk about the past and the way he built up the company from scratch.'

'Does Roger resent your being the Managing Director instead of himself?'

'Probably. But he's too young for the job and I doubt if he would ever have had sufficient authority. There's more to running a company than knowing how it works. You have to have massive energy and the ability to inspire others.'

'I'm sure *you* are an inspiration to everyone who works for you.'

His look was sharp, but she returned it wide-eyed, and he let it go unanswered.

It was not until a week later that he told her Gina and Charles had invited them to dinner, and though she longed to refuse she knew it was impossible. To do so might make Charles suspicious and also break the bargain she had entered into with Luke: to act the part of his wife. She was intelligent enough to know that her reluctance to accept the invitation stemmed from her antipathy towards Gina, but this feeling did not seem to be reciprocated, for at their eventual meeting, later in the week, Gina's greeting was as warm as usual, though the blue eyes could not hide their astonishment at the change in Emily's appearance. But no comment was made until Charles did so, and it brought an immediate frown—almost as immediately disguised—to the lovely face.

'Marriage agrees with you, my dear,' Charles exclaimed. 'You look enchanting.'

'Thanks to a new hairdresser and new clothes,' Emily smiled.

'To say you've turned into a beautiful swan implies that

you were once an ugly duckling, but I——'

'On the contrary,' Luke intervened, coming to stand beside Emily and putting his arm on her shoulder, as though he really were her loving bridegroom. 'She is a swan now because she was a little gosling before!'

'Well said, old chap,' Charles chuckled, and motioned Luke to serve the drinks from the tray on the sideboard.

Luke did so, and looked so at home dispensing them that Emily was sickened. How cleverly he and Gina had pulled the wool over Charles's eyes. Again she wondered why he had allowed himself to become involved in such a messy situation. One could not always guide one's heart, but once he had discovered he was in love with Gina surely it would have been better to have left Harricks? She did not believe he had refused to do so because he was afraid of being unable to find a job of equal importance, and this led her to the conclusion that Gina had forced him to stay. Under cover of the conversation she studied Gina, bitterly acknowledging that her beauty alone was enough to make any man lose his senses. Reed-slender and with her vivid colouring, she was a picture of sensual delight. No wonder Luke was her devoted slave; loving her so much that he was prepared to live a lie. This not only indicated his strength of mind but also his depth of passion for her; deep enough to destroy his sense of right and wrong.

The door opened and Emily's fingers tightened on the glass as she recognised Roger Harrick. Accepting a drink from Luke, he sat beside her. Tensely she waited for him to speak, anticipating some snide comment on her marriage. She was not wrong, for it came at once.

'I'm glad to see you didn't totally waste your honeymoon. At least you took advantage of the shops!'

Emily hid her hands in the folds of her skirt. She was wearing one of her Paris dresses: a long-skirted crêpe, the flowing lines making her look even more petite. 'If you want to start a verbal battle with me, Mr. Harrick, I'd better warn you I was head of the Debating Society in my final year.'

'Is that supposed to frighten me?'

'It should, if you have any sense!'

His pale skin flushed, making him look younger and less sure of himself. Though she guessed him to be in his late twenties, she felt immeasurably older than him, and because of it lost some of her anger.

'You've got what you wanted,' she said softly. 'Luke has a wife and he isn't seeing Gina any more.'

'But what sort of wife? Someone to whom he'll remain faithful or something he'll use as a cover while he and Gina carry on as before? I've a good mind to tell my uncle the truth!'

'You'd never do that.'

His eyes narrowed. 'What makes you so sure?'

'Because you wouldn't want to live the rest of your life knowing you're a murderer! And you would be,' she re-iterated, driving the point home. 'Charles is a sick man and he couldn't withstand the shock.'

He did not reply, but the way he avoided her eyes told her she had scored. The knowledge made her wonder if Luke had tried to call Roger's bluff. Still, if he had done, she would not be here now, married to him and hopelessly in love with him.

'You're right, Mrs. Adams.' Roger's voice was barely suitable. 'I'd never do anything to hurt my uncle. But you'd do well to warn Luke that if he thinks he can carry on as before, he'd better think again.'

'My husband has no intention of carrying on as before,' Emily lied with bravura. 'He has *me* to reckon with now.'

Roger could not help a grim smile. 'You?'

'Me,' she said firmly.

Roger looked as if he wanted to say something more, but before he could speak dinner was announced, and during the meal he was placed across the table from her. Afterwards, when they returned to the drawing-room for coffee, the conversation still remained general, but as she left the room to collect her coat, he waylaid her in the hall.

'Will you have lunch with me if I telephone you, Mrs.

Adams?'

Surprised by the request, she nodded and hurried up-stairs. She was slipping on the white mink jacket when Gina came into the bedroom.

'Emily darling, I haven't had a chance to speak to you alone all evening.'

'It's just as well,' Emily retorted. 'I don't think we have anything to say to each other.'

'Don't be old-fashioned and silly. You aren't still blaming me for what I did, are you? After all, I thought I was doing you a good turn. I didn't force you to marry Luke. You did it because you wanted the money.'

It was too valid a remark to deny, and it put Emily at a disadvantage. 'None of us have come out of this episode very well,' she agreed. 'But I don't think *my* reason for doing what I did was quite as despicable as yours and Luke's.'

Gina sank down on the bed, her face uneasy and pale, and Emily realised that the evening had not been easy for her. Loving Luke as she undoubtedly did must have made it galling for her to see him with a wife, even if she herself had found him the wife, and knew his marriage to be a contract without meaning.

'An impartial observer—if they were judging what we did——' Gina continued, 'would say Luke and I love Charles more than we love each other, and that our concern not to hurt him outweighed our own happiness.'

'Luke could have gone out of your life.'

'He *would* have done if there had been no other solution! But marrying you seemed to solve the problem. You've got to admit it solved your problem too, so don't stand there talking to me as if *we're* a dungheap and *you* are smelling of roses!' Gina gave a forced laugh. 'There, you've made me lose my temper, and that's something I always try not to do. It gives me frown lines.'

Irritably Emily walked to the door. 'I don't want to quarrel with you, Gina. It's pointless. I don't want to be friends with you either.'

'Why not? By rights you should be grateful to me. Ten thousand pounds for marrying Luke isn't a sum of money to be sneezed at.'

'I have no intention of taking the other five thousand pounds,' Emily snapped.

'Why not? By the time your marriage is annulled I'm sure you'll have earned it.'

'What's that supposed to mean?'

'Luke isn't the easiest man in the world to live with. And as he isn't in love with you, he's likely to be even more difficult.'

'I haven't noticed him being difficult so far,' Emily said coldly. 'The reverse, in fact.'

The red-gold head tilted sharply. 'He's still on his best behaviour with you, darling. But don't expect him to act the normal husband.'

'Would you like me to tell you when he does?'

The blue eyes glittered. 'You *are* sharp tonight.' With a graceful movement Gina glided across to her. 'You wouldn't have fallen for him yourself, would you?'

'Don't be ridiculous.' Emily opened the bedroom door, but Gina was not to be put off so easily, and kept pace with her as she walked down the corridor.

'Why is it ridiculous, darling? Luke's very good-looking and you aren't in love with anyone else.'

'Just because *you* find him attractive, don't assume every woman does.'

'But you *do* find him attractive, don't you?'

'No,' Emily said, and then knowing the answer was childish, corrected it. 'Yes, of course he is, but—but he's not my type. I prefer someone more like—more like Roger.'

Gina laughed. 'How amusing if you and Roger fell for each other. It would give everybody a happy ending!'

'For heaven's sake, stop talking rubbish!' Emily resorted to schoolgirl vernacular in an effort to restore the conversation to normality. It did the trick, for they went down the stairs without speaking.

Luke was waiting in the hall and Emily flung him a cold

120

look before going back into the drawing-room to say good-night to Charles, who was lying on the settee.

'I'm sorry we stayed so late,' she said, bending over to kiss him.

'Don't apologise, dear child. I regard you and Luke as part of my family, and I'm quite relaxed with you. I only get tired when I'm with strangers.' He squeezed her hand. 'Come again soon. I enjoy seeing you.'

Sitting beside Luke in the car, Emily forgot Charles, and wondered instead if Luke resented having her beside him instead of Gina. But he made no reference to it and merely commended her on the way she had drawn Roger out.

'I've never known him so relaxed and comfortable with anyone. He's generally nervous and unsure of himself.'

'I don't see why he should be.'

'Because he wants to run before he can walk. If your ambitions outweigh your maturity, you either develop an inferiority complex or a superiority one.'

'My, my,' she drawled, 'we *have* studied our Freud!'

He chuckled and negotiated a corner. He rarely kept the chauffeur on at night, and he handled the car with ease, controlling it as competently as he no doubt controlled all the situations with which he had to deal.

'You know I'm speaking the truth,' he continued. 'By rights, Roger should have worked his way up from the bottom; not come in at executive level. I suggested it to him, but he thought I was trying to prevent him from getting his just deserts.'

'I'm sure you would love to give Roger his just deserts!'

'Because of the ultimatum he gave me?' Luke shook his head. 'As a matter of fact I wasn't thinking of that at all. I was discussing Roger simply as a young man who works for the company. My own feelings don't come into it.'

She knew he was speaking the truth; knew too that this ability to compartmentalise his mind, to close off facts he did not want to worry about, and to concentrate only on those that were important at the moment, was part of his strength. This of course enabled him to pursue divers business transactions without letting his involvement in one influence his position in another. He would be able to keep his emotional life sealed off in the same way; a facility which was rarely enjoyed by any woman, for love was usually her whole existence, colouring her thoughts and actions, as her own love for Luke coloured hers.

'I don't blame Roger for seeing himself in your shoes,' she said matter-of-factly. 'After all, he *is* Charles's only living relative.'

'But not one tenth as capable as his uncle. In ten years' time he might make a good second-in-command, but never more than that. He should have gone in for farming, which is what he originally planned to do.'

'Why did he change his mind?'

'Because Charles fell ill and asked him to join the company. He felt it important that there should be someone called Harrick to carry on.'

'But now he's happy to have *you* carry on?'

'Yes,' Luke said. 'I'm extremely lucky in my relationship with Charles. That makes my love for Gina all the more difficult.'

'I'd rather not talk about it.'

He drove for a couple of hundred yards in silence before he spoke again. 'It isn't like you to run away from facts, Emily.'

'I'm not running away from them. I just don't see the point in our discussing them. I know how you and Gina feel about each other and I know that when—that the moment you're free you'll want to marry her. So what's there to discuss?'

'Put like that,' he conceded, 'there's nothing to talk about. But I don't like to feel we can't be honest with each other.'

'We have different ideas of what honesty means.'

'You have a remarkable facility for hitting below the belt,' he said curtly, and this time said no more until he had parked the car in the garage below their block of flats and went up with her in the lift. 'I'd like us to start giving a few

122

dinner parties, Emily. If you call my secretary tomorrow she'll give you a list of the people I want to invite. There are about three dozen in all. If you can arrange five or six dinners it shouldn't be too much for Mrs. Evans to manage.'

'Are there any particular people you'd like me to invite first?'

'Miss Godfrey can tell you about that when she gives you the list. You won't go far wrong if you take her advice.' He hesitated. 'It won't be too much for you to do, will it?'

'On the contrary. As a matter of fact I was beginning to think of taking a job.'

'You have a job here.'

'Not a very rewarding one.' Instantly she thought of the five thousand pounds he had given her, and knew from his expression that he had thought the same. 'I'll call your secretary in the morning,' she said hastily, and murmuring goodnight, went to her room.

Though Luke had spoken confidently of his Mrs. Evans being able to cope with the dinner parties he wished to give, Emily found that she was not disposed towards entertaining, nor as capable of doing it as he believed.

'I came here because Mr. Adams was a bachelor,' she said truculently when Emily went to the kitchen to discuss the menus for the first dinner party. 'And he said then that there'd be no entertaining at all.'

'At that time my husband had not envisaged having a hostess. But now he has, he wishes to invite people to his home.'

'Those weren't the terms on which I was engaged. Mr. Adams knows very well——'

'Mr. Adams knows very well what he wants,' Emily interrupted, 'and if you don't wish to remain here under these terms, then you had better find another position.'

The woman looked taken aback. 'Are you giving me my notice?'

'Yes.' Emily hoped she was doing the right thing, but decided there was no point having a cook who only wished to cater for two people. 'I don't know how you're paid, but——'

'Weekly, madam.'

'Then you may leave on Friday.'

'You won't find it easy to get anyone else. How will you manage?' Seeing the end of her job in sight, Mrs. Evans appeared to regret her earlier truculence. 'I'm willing to stay if you will engage a kitchen maid to help me.'

'No, thank you. I prefer to find someone else.'

Looking through the classified telephone directory for domestic agencies, Emily knew it would not be as easy to replace the housekeeper as she had pretended. But she resolutely made one call after another, and only with her eighth one did she have a stroke of luck. The agency had one person available who had contacted them that very morning. Her employer had died six months ago and she had decided to retire, but had found it so boring that she now wished to resume work.

'I'm afraid I can't give you any personal recommendation,' the woman at the agency explained, 'but she seems pleasant and it would certainly be worth your while to see her. Her name is Mrs. Winters. She worked—and still lives—in a village near Cambridge.'

'You mean Mary Winters!' Emily could not hide her excitement. 'She worked for Colonel Moreton—in the same village where *I* used to live. I'll take her the moment she's willing to come.'

'I'll call her and arrange an interview.'

'There's no need to do that. I'll go and see her myself.'

'I don't think——'

'I'll pay your fee, of course,' Emily interrupted.

'In that case,' said the woman graciously, 'I'll leave you to make your own arrangements.'

Determined not to lose someone whom she had always known to be a treasure, Emily decided to go to Little Manning immediately. Mary Winters was not on the telephone, but it was unlikely that she would be out, and even if she were, she would not be far. Changing into a warm coat,

124

Emily telephoned for a taxi to take her to the station.

It was a strange feeling to return to the village after a month's absence, and she went at once to her cottage to make sure everything was aired and clean. For the moment, she was keeping it closed, but in the past few weeks she had changed so much that she was no longer sure she wanted to resume her life in a village community when her marriage was over. Once she was parted from Luke she would want to keep herself occupied the whole time, and this meant finding a position that would tax her far more than the work she had been doing when she was single.

Locking the door of the cottage, she went down the single High Street which the village boasted and turned into the winding lane that led to Mary Winters' cottage: small and thatched, it looked as if it had been built to make a picture postcard. Its owner was equally picturesque, short and plump, with grey hair plaited around her head and a rosy-cheeked face which creased into a smile of delight as she heard the reason for Emily's visit.

Mary Winters had no hesitation in accepting the job, and though she had never lived in an apartment, she was confident she would get used to it.

'The main thing is for me to be happy with the people I look after. I was so many years with Colonel Moreton ... Still, I've known *you*, Miss Emily, all your life. Begging your pardon,' she said hastily. 'You're Mrs. Adams now. The other name slipped out.'

'Don't worry about it,' Emily smiled. 'Just tell me when you can come to London.'

An hour later Emily was on her way back to town. All arrangements had been made and Luke's chauffeur would be collecting Mary Winters on Saturday and bringing her to the flat.

It was later than Emily had intended when she arrived home. She had missed the last non-stop train and had been obliged to change twice and to wait an interminable length of time for a connection. It was well past eight-thirty when she put her key in the latch, and as she entered the hall

Luke strode out to greet her. He was paler than she had ever seen him and his eyes glittered like chips of ice.

'Where have you been?' he said angrily.

'I went to Little Manning.'

'Without telling anyone? Couldn't you have left word where you were going and what time you were coming back?'

'I expected to be home before you. But I missed my train.'

He swung back into the living-room and she followed him, not knowing why he should be so angry.

'Is there anything wrong?' she asked carefully. 'Charles hasn't . . .'

'Charles is all right,' he said quietly. 'I was worried about *you*. I thought you had had an accident.'

Surprise rendered her speechless, and as it ebbed, it was replaced by delight. Luke had been worried about her. It was incredible, but she must not show any awareness of it. 'I'm quite capable of looking after myself,' she said carefully.

'Maybe so, but you are my wife and I don't want you running around England in the middle of winter.'

The words were so ludicrous that she smiled.

'What's funny about that?' he glared.

'You're behaving like an irate hen!' she replied, and was unable to stop a giggle.

If possible he looked even angrier, but just when she thought he was going to explode he suddenly relaxed. 'Not a hen,' he corrected. 'At least give me the honour of being a cockerel!'

This time she laughed outright, and though he did not exactly join in, he did allow himself to smile.

'You look cold and tired,' he said. 'Come to the fire and get warm while I pour you a drink.'

Sipping her sherry, she told him of her reason for going to Little Manning, and though he showed anxiety at hearing of Mrs. Evans' behaviour, this gave way to relief when she recounted her discovery of Mary Winters.

'The gods must have been smiling on you today,' he murmured. 'A good cook is as hard to find as a nugget of gold.'

'It isn't only because she's a good cook that I'm so pleased. It's because she's willing and kind. That's extremely important. There's nothing worse than having someone around you who is resentful.'

'How right you are!'

His look was so keen that she knew he was referring to her own attitude to him, and because she was honest she did not pretend to misunderstand him. 'I will always try to fulfil the bargain I made with you,' she said primly. 'If I do anything you don't like, I hope you will tell me.'

'Thank you, Emily. The same goes for me too. Though I'm sure I don't need to add the rest of your sentence. I know that if I do anything you don't like, you'll have no hesitation in letting me know!'

'You make me sound a real termagant,' she sighed.

'Only a very small one!' He saw her eyes flash and laughed. 'I do wish you would stop hankering for extra inches. You suit me very well the way you are.'

Wishing she really did suit him, Emily stood up and said she was going to change for dinner.

'Why bother?' he asked carelessly. 'There's only the two of us. Unless you *want* to change, of course.'

'I wouldn't mind getting into a housecoat,' she said frankly. 'I'm still cold after hanging round those freezing stations.'

'Then hurry and do so. Dinner has been waiting an hour.'

She hurried out, rejoining him within moments in the dining-room. His frank look indicated his appreciation of her soft wool housecoat, its variegated shades of pink lending colour to her skin. Her cheeks still glowed from the cold and they remained bright throughout the meal. It was the first time they had dined alone since their return from Paris, for on other nights Luke had either come home late —having dined at his club with a business associate—or brought someone with him from the office.

127

'I've enjoyed this evening very much,' he said later as they sat on either side of the fireplace. 'I don't usually relax like this.'

'So I've noticed. Don't you ever get tired of working?'

'I get more tired when I don't! Work is my hobby.'

'Do you never hanker for university life?'

'Occasionally. But I know I wouldn't have the patience to remain there for long. I have inherited my liking for business from my mother's family.'

'Do you ever see your relations?'

'Usually at Christmas. I have a load of cousins in Yorkshire.'

'Gina's family come from Yorkshire.' As Emily spoke she wished she could retract the words, afraid that the mention of Gina would make Luke withdraw into his shell again. But if anything he relaxed even more, for her words reminded him that it was through Gina's family that he had first met Charles.

'A cousin of Gina's was a student of mine at Cambridge,' he said, 'and he invited me to spend a weekend with him. Gina and Charles were there, and the rest you know.'

'I don't. I only know that you suddenly went to work for him.'

Luke rubbed the side of his face, and she noticed the faint shadow of stubble on it and wondered if his skin was rough to the touch. She knew a longing to put her fingers against his face, and forced the thought away.

'Tell me how Charles persuaded you to leave the Groves of Academe,' she said hurriedly. 'Did he dangle a bag of gold in front of you?'

'Charles would never be as crude as that!' Luke smiled. 'He invited me to London for dinner and introduced me to a friend of his called Adrian Harrison. You've heard of his company, no doubt.'

'No doubt,' Emily said dryly, for Adrian Harrison was one of the biggest publishers of educational books.

'Harrison asked me to do a book about the City,' Luke continued. 'To trace its history and the effect of its financial importance upon the country's economy. That was the carrot in front of the donkey. In order to write the book I had to learn much more about the City than I already knew, and the more I learned, the more fascinated I became with it. The book was a success and I was asked to follow it up with one about the six biggest industrial firms in the country.'

'And that was when the donkey ate the carrot?' she said.

'Exactly! After that, all Charles had to do was to rope me in!' The blue eyes narrowed. 'He must have been very far-seeing to have recognised my potential.'

Far-seeing in business only, Emily thought bitterly, and was suddenly glad that in other respects Charles was blind. If he were not, he would have guessed long ago that Gina did not love him; would probably have realised she loved Luke. And being Charles, if he *had* guessed, he would have gracefully removed himself from her life. 'In which case I wouldn't be here with Luke,' Emily knew, and swallowing the realisation, said: 'No wonder Charles feels paternalistic towards you. He was your Pygmalion.'

'And I am yours!' Luke leaned forward and touched her silky black hair, allowing his fingers to linger on it momentarily before drawing back. 'The change in you is quite remarkable.'

'I'm the same Emily Lamb inside,' she said breathlessly, and went quickly to the door. 'It's late, Luke, and I'm tired.'

'I'm not,' he said. 'You always refresh me.'

She blinked quickly, too moved to speak, and his words remained with her as she lay in bed and stared out at the dark, storm-tossed sky.

CHAPTER TEN

EMILY stared round the restaurant and seeing several pairs of eyes regarding her with interest, hastily turned back to her companion and smiled at him. Roger Harrick smiled back.

'I'm so glad you were able to have lunch with me today,' he said. 'I hope you didn't mind my asking you at such short notice?'

'I was glad you asked me. It's broken up the boredom of the day.'

'You don't look the type to be bored.'

'I never thought I could be,' she said candidly, 'but then I've never lived the life of the idle rich until now.' She stared round the restaurant again. 'Look at everyone enjoying themselves on expense account lunches—what a waste of time it all is!'

'Sometimes more business gets done over a lunch table than in an office.'

'Only because the luncheon table is available!'

'You're talking like a tax inspector!'

She laughed. 'I don't mean to. I'm just cheesed off. I really will find myself something to do.'

'When you told me you were a social worker I couldn't believe it. You look far too fragile and exotic to have worked for a living.'

'You should have seen me before I married Luke. I didn't look half so exotic then.'

'I don't believe it.'

'It's true.'

'Are you happy in your marriage?'

She had been half expecting the question, but the bluntness of it took her by surprise, and she looked down at her hands and twisted the wedding ring on her finger. It was a narrow circlet of diamonds, one of the most expensive baubles Luke had bought her.

'You haven't answered me, Emily,' Roger said.

'What bride would ever admit to being unhappy?'

'You aren't a real bride.'

'Do you find it so inconceivable that Luke should genuinely like me?'

'You know I didn't mean that,' he said at once. 'Quite the opposite, in fact. But any man who is stupid enough to fall for Gina——'

'You're speaking about a friend of mine.'

'Is she still?'

'What do you mean?'

'It's obvious Gina drummed up the whole thing. She must have thought of you the minute she heard my ultimatum to Luke. And I must say it was pretty clever of her. If you want to make sure of your lover, marry him off to your best friend.'

The diamond circlet on Emily's finger winked with a thousand lights and she quickly blinked the tears from her eyes. 'Do you mind if we change the subject? I find it an unpleasant one.'

'I'm sorry.' Roger looked genuinely concerned. 'I assumed you wouldn't mind talking about it.'

'Well, I do.' She forced herself to pick up her knife and fork, but it was an effort to eat food that tasted as if it were made of sawdust, and she resolutely chewed and swallowed without having any idea of what she was eating. She was aware of Roger looking at her with ill-concealed curiosity, as if he could not believe the picture he was forming. Was he upset because he did not dislike her as he had anticipated he would? It was obvious that his invitation to take her out to lunch had been prompted partly by curiosity and partly by a desire to get to know her. In an odd way she felt she was dining with her marriage broker, for he, more than anybody else, was responsible for her becoming Luke's wife.

'Why are you smiling?' Roger asked.

'I was thinking I have you to thank for my marriage.'

'If *I* had seen you first, Luke would never have had the chance.'

'There's nothing like a Paris hair-do for bringing out the wolf in a man!'

'I'm not flirting with you.' Roger looked boyish and uncomfortable. 'I mean it.'

'You'd better put it in writing!'

'I intend to say it to you so often that it won't be necessary for me to write it down.'

'Do you always talk to married women like this?'

'You're the first married woman I've ever taken out. Besides, I don't regard you as properly married.'

'Are you calling me improper?' she teased deliberately.

He signalled the wine waiter to replenish their glasses and waited until he had done so before speaking again. 'I don't see you marrying a man you didn't love—but on the other hand you seem too intelligent to have been fooled by Luke. Maybe you also had reasons for getting married.'

She smiled but refused to be drawn on the subject. Roger could assume what he liked about her marriage to Luke, but as long as she did not answer his questions he wouldn't know whether he was right. She didn't understand her reluctance to tell him the truth and wondered if it was a fear that by doing so she might lessen her chance of making Luke fall in love with her. As long as she could pretend her marriage was real, perhaps it might eventually become so. Hard on this thought came anger with herself. She would do far better to face the truth and accept Gina's invincibility. No girl could compete with such beauty and self-assurance. Wryly she wondered what Luke's friends would think if they knew the truth. Since Mary Winters' advent into their life a month ago, they had done a great deal of entertaining, and she knew that she and Luke had given the impression of contentment and happiness. Sometimes as she looked at him she wondered if it was *all* an act on his part, but she had never yet been able to find a satisfactory answer to the question. Perhaps, like her, he could close his mind to the truth and believe what he wanted to believe.

Maybe this was why he could pretend to be a devoted husband. It was a performance which, had it been on film, would have earned him an Oscar. But then as a clever business man he was used to simulation and she would do well to remember this.

'There's Luke,' Roger said. 'He's just come in.'

Emily turned quickly and saw Luke threading his way between the tables to sit at one by the window. His companion was an elderly man and they both looked rather sombre.

'It's Wilson,' Roger explained. 'He's been trying to wean Luke away from Harricks for months.'

'Luke would never leave Charles,' Emily said firmly.

'He would have had to leave if he hadn't married you,' Roger said bluntly.

Emily forced herself not to reply, and watched Luke as he studied the menu. His glance at it was brief—as if he had already decided what to eat and did not wish to waste time thinking about it—and he set down the card and let his gaze move idly across the room. She knew he was unaware that she was here but was instantly able to tell when he spotted her, for she saw his start of recognition and, even at a distance, could discern the colour that ran into his face. Then he stood up, murmured something to his companion and wended his way purposefully through the tables towards her.

'I didn't know you were lunching here, Emily,' he said as he reached her side.

'I didn't know either until mid-morning. Roger rang me unexpectedly.'

'Indeed?' There was disbelief in Luke's voice and animosity too. Somehow it didn't surprise her, for she knew he had little reason to like Roger; unlike herself who had every reason to be grateful to him.

'I hope you'll join us for coffee?' Luke was speaking again, including Roger in the invitation although he was looking directly at Emily.

Not sure what the protocol was in this matter, Emily

133

glanced at Roger and he nodded imperceptibly.

'That would be very nice, Luke,' she said quietly. 'Give us a nod when you've reached the dessert stage and we'll come over and join you.'

Still smiling slightly, Luke returned to his table, but she could tell from the set of his shoulders that he was far from pleased at seeing her here. She forced herself not to read jealousy into his reaction; more likely it was a 'dog in the manger' attitude at seeing one of his possessions—even an unloved one—with another male.

'What bad luck for us to meet Luke here,' Roger said. 'Now I won't be able to have you to myself.'

'You're a very unsubtle Romeo,' she retorted.

He chuckled. 'And you are devastatingly blunt.'

'It's part of my charm.'

'Actually it is. You're refreshingly candid, Emily, and in these days of plastic people, your honesty makes you stand out.'

'A half-pint like me needs something to make me noticeable,' she added.

'Your smallness is part of your charm too.'

'Don't tell me I make all the men in my life feel big and strong!'

'I bet you do.'

'Then you've lost the bet,' she said with honesty. 'All the men I met looked on me as a good sport.'

'I don't believe your past is as unromantic as you make it sound.'

'It was extremely unromantic,' she assured him. 'That's why I enjoyed working for Gina. It gave me a glimpse of the way the other half lived.'

'And now you're the other half!'

'But I still feel the same.' She paused. 'Not quite the same, though. Knowing you look your best does wonders for your ego.'

'I'm a good ego builder too.'

She widened her eyes at him and her long black lashes stuck out straight as a doll's. 'Are you purposely flirting with me, Roger?'

'Do you object?'

'Why should I? But you'll be wasting your time.'

'I don't think so.' Though he was still smiling there was an intenseness in his face that was not humorous at all. 'I plan to remain in your life, Emily; to become a dependable friend, a shoulder to lean on.'

'Luke will be delighted to know that.'

'I'm thinking of the time when Luke . . .' He stopped, and though she knew what he had refrained from saying, she refused to let him see that she did, and made a great show of choosing a sweet from the trolley that had been wheeled to a stop in front of her.

'For a little girl you certainly knock back your food,' he commented, eyeing a plate heaped with almond gateau, trifle and ice-cream, which the waiter set in front of her.

'Everybody says that,' she grinned.

'Oh dear, I thought I was being original.'

'Then you'll have to try harder. And that applies to your other remarks too—the dependable friend bit. It went out with the flappers!'

Roger's features sharpened, making him look the way he had when she had first met him. 'You don't mince your words, do you, Emily?'

'Candour is part of my charm, remember?'

'And you rub salt in the wound too!'

She laughed. 'Every positive has a negative.'

'I'm beginning to find out. Just don't hit me when I'm down!'

'I always try to play by the Queensberry rules.' She glanced over his shoulder. 'Luke would like us to join him. Do you mind if we do?'

'Would it make any difference if I did?'

Shaking her head, she rose and moved over to the table by the window.

In Luke's presence Emily noticed that Roger appeared very much the young man lunching with his superior. It was not surprising since Luke *was* his superior, not only in work but in every other way too. But then, Emily thought soberly, Luke made every man look insignificant. It was a chastening admission and boded ill for her future.

'I hope you and Luke will dine with me one evening?' Mr. Wilson was looking in her direction, and she forced herself to concentrate on what he was saying. 'Which evening would suit you best?'

'You'd better ask my husband.'

Mr. Wilson turned to Luke. 'You have a diplomatic wife, Luke.'

'A well-trained one,' he replied.

'I prefer the word diplomatic to well-trained,' Emily intervened, and everyone laughed.

Roger glanced at his watch and stood up. 'I have an appointment at the office, I'm afraid. Do please excuse me.'

Immediately Emily stood up with him and Luke frowned at her. 'There's no need for you to go, too.'

'I must,' she smiled. 'Anyway, I'm sure you and Mr. Wilson have things to talk about.'

Luke looked as if he were going to protest, but he thought better of it, though his kiss on her cheek before she walked away, surprised her.

'You didn't need to leave with me,' Roger remarked as they climbed into the waiting taxi.

'You brought me here,' she replied.

'Are you always so careful about the social p's and q's?'

'I don't like hurting people's pride.'

'I just think you don't like hurting people.'

She blushed at the compliment, appreciating it far more than the fulsome ones he had previously paid to her.

'Will you let me see you again?' he asked.

'Why do you want to?' He stared at her with such astonishment that she felt emboldened to explain herself. 'Are you taking me out because you think it will irritate Luke or because you genuinely want to see me again?'

Roger went scarlet. 'Annoying Luke might have been the reason before I met you, but it doesn't apply any more. It's you I'm interested in; and as for offending Luke—all I can say is I wish he'd never come into your life.'

'Then you wouldn't have met me either.'

He sighed. 'Which goes to show that every cloud has a silver lining.' He caught her hand as it lay on her lap. 'I hope the cloud blows away soon, Emily. Even though . . .'

His voice trailed away and she realised that he was aware that this would only happen when his uncle died and Luke and Gina were free to marry.

'You're very fond of your uncle, aren't you?' she said quietly.

'Yes. My father died when I was nine and Uncle Charles has looked after me ever since.'

It was on the tip of her tongue to ask him whether he felt that by right of succession alone he should be where Luke was now. But there was no way of doing so diplomatically, and she said no more until the taxi drew to a stop outside her block of flats.

'I suppose you're always busy in the evening,' Roger murmured as he walked with her to the entrance.

'Even if I weren't, I wouldn't see you. It wouldn't be wise.'

'Are you worried at what people might say?'

'I'd be worried at what Luke would say!'

'Would he care?'

It was the most direct remark Roger had made, but as with his other pertinent ones she took it at face value. 'What new husband wouldn't?'

'Don't keep up the act with me,' he said roughly. 'I know damn well he only married you to keep his position with the company!'

'Goodbye, Roger,' she said, and held out her hand. 'Thank you for a lovely lunch.'

'When can I see you again?'

'Call me.' She pulled her hand away from his and hurried inside, aware of him watching her until the elevator doors blocked her from his sight.

It would be easy to be flattered by Roger's attentions, but she was still not sure whether he was genuinely attracted to

137

her—as he proclaimed—or if it stemmed from his desire to needle Luke. This brought her back to Luke's behaviour in the restaurant which, had she not known him better, she might have mistaken for jealousy. But it was dangerous to go on thinking about it, for her foolish heart could give her false hope which, when it died, would only lead to greater unhappiness for her. Resolutely she concentrated on the evening ahead. They were giving another dinner party and she went into the kitchen to see if there was anything she could do.

As usual Mrs. Winters had everything under control: pots bubbled gently on top of the stove and in the butler's pantry the silver and crockery—pristine and gleaming—were ready to be set out in the dining-room. Knowing there was nothing for her to do except dress and make herself pretty, Emily went to do so. It was a pity her father couldn't see her now, she mused, as she opened her wardrobe and chose one of her many lovely dresses. How pleased he would be by the luxury and beauty of her surroundings. Most important of all, how much he would have enjoyed Luke's formidable intelligence. Almost immediately this made her wonder what Luke saw in Gina. Yet because a man was intelligent it didn't mean he wanted intelligence in the woman he loved. More often than not he would settle for beauty alone. Not that Gina was as foolish or as innocent as she pretended. But nor was she intelligent in the accepted sense of the word; it was a cunning typical of many women of her type; based on self-preservation and the desire for security. This alone prompted her every action.

The telephone rang and Emily, crossing the hall to her bedroom, picked it up. It was Gina, and she had to force herself not to put down the receiver without speaking.

'Why haven't you been to see me?' Gina said without preamble. 'You're acting as if I were a stranger.'

'You are.'

'Don't be ridiculous. Just because I didn't tell you the whole story about Luke and myself . . .'

'The *whole* story?' Emily exploded. 'You told me nothing! If you were a genuine friend of mine you would have told me the truth and let *me* decide whether or not I wanted to get involved in your affair.'

'I was afraid that if you knew the truth, you wouldn't help me.'

'All the more reason for you not to have lied to me.'

'Emily darling, be reasonable. Can't you see you were the ideal girl to marry Luke? The one person I can trust to do the right thing when I'm free to . . .' The soft voice became huskier. 'Please, Emily, I miss not seeing you. I thought it would be fun to have you living in London. There are so many things we can do together. I'm giving a party next week and you know exactly the way I like the flowers done.'

Emily could not help smiling. Gina missed having a part-time social secretary and hoped she could still cajole her into doing it. 'I don't need to earn any money now, Gina,' she said clearly, 'but I can recommend a good agency if you're looking for someone.'

There was a pause and Emily could visualise Gina frowning, not sure whether to take offence or to pretend she had not understood the implication of the remark.

'Now you're being silly,' Gina said, taking the latter course. 'You are the only person who knows how I feel about Luke, so you're the only one with whom I can relax. I'm surprised at you for letting pride stop you from being friends with me.'

'I didn't think we were ever friends, Gina. You used me.'

The pause this time was longer, and when Gina spoke again her voice was less placatory. 'You're being extremely bitchy, Emily. Maybe it isn't pride you're suffering from, but unrequited love.'

'You seem determined to prove me in love with your boy-friend.'

'That's the most obvious reason for your being so spite-ful.' There was a fine edge of temper to Gina's voice. 'Per-haps you do want Luke for yourself. That could explain

139

why you're so angry with me.'

The receiver trembled in Emily's hand, but she forced herself to remain calm. She must never let Gina guess how right she was.

'Well, darling,' Gina purred, 'aren't you going to deny what I've said?'

'I will when I can get my breath back,' Emily said lightly. 'At the moment I'm astonished. Still, I suppose it's easier for you to believe I don't want to see you because I love Luke than to admit I'm disgusted with *you*.'

'A good try, Emily, but it won't work. If your emotions weren't involved, your pride wouldn't be hurt. You have obviously fallen for my lover!'

'If it makes you happy to think so, then you must think it. Now if you will excuse me, I'd like to go.'

'Of course, darling,' Gina laughed. 'Just remember you'll never get him no matter how hard you try. He's mine and he'll remain mine.'

'Goodbye, Gina,' Emily replied gently, and putting down the telephone, retreated to the sanctuary of her room. Only here did she give way to anger, pacing the carpet with quick steps and wishing she had the chance to throttle Gina or Luke; or better still, both of them.

The closing of the front door told her Luke had come home, and glancing at her watch she saw it was time to change. She was not his wife in the real sense of the word, but she was nonetheless his hostess, and a good hostess was always ready and waiting to greet her guests.

In the event she was in the living-room a few moments before Luke joined her. His silver-blond hair was wet from his shower and gleamed like metal. It made him look more handsome than ever and she could well understand how Gina had felt when she had realised that the only way to keep him was either to leave Charles or to find him a temporary wife. It would have taken great courage or great certainty of his love to have allowed him to leave the company and move into a different milieu. He was not a man to be without female companionship for long, and it was not surprising that Gina had hit upon the idea of using her dowdy little school friend as a watchdog. Who would she have chosen if she hadn't known me? Emily wondered. Some other little mouse; a nobody, willing to play the part for a price? But what would Luke's reactions have been to a Miss Nobody? Though not a snob, he would never have married anyone who did not fit into his world. Yet how had he evaluated her own potential? They had barely spoken half a dozen sentences before he had asked her if she were willing to enter into a business marriage with him. Had he done this because he had recognised that she could be turned into a swan by a change of make-up, a new wardrobe and a clever hairdresser?

'You seemed to be enjoying yourself with Roger,' Luke broke into her thoughts. 'You never told me you were lunching with him.'

'I told you I didn't know it myself until he rang me this morning.'

'You went with him at short notice.'

'Why not? My diary isn't crammed with engagements.'

Luke went to the sideboard and, as she shook her head, poured himself a whisky. Holding it, he came to sit beside her. 'From that remark I take it you're bored?'

'I'm ready to climb up the wall,' she confessed. 'I wanted to talk to you again about my taking a part-time job.'

'Your job is to look after me,' he said flatly.

'We have staff for that.'

'You know what I mean.'

'I do,' she said equably. 'But do you know what I mean? You can't expect me to twiddle my thumbs around the flat all day.'

'There are lots of charities you can work for.'

'Organise fêtes and bazaars with well-corseted matrons. Have a heart, Luke! You know I can do something more worthwhile than that.'

'Isn't it worthwhile to be a wife?'

'A real one, yes,' she said bluntly. 'But not a make-

141

believe one.'

His breath hissed sharply between his teeth. 'I was wondering when you would be coming round to that! At the risk of being repetitive, I must remind you that you've been well paid for it. And also that no one forced you to accept my offer.'

'I don't regret it,' she said quickly. 'But I don't see why I can't fulfil my part of the bargain and still do some social work.'

'What would happen if I asked you to come away with me on a business trip? I frequently go away for a couple of weeks at a time—also the odd week-end when it's often an advantage to have your wife with you. And then we entertain a lot here. I know we have good staff, but you do all the organising.' He rubbed his hand along the side of his face. 'I don't want to be difficult, but I don't see how you can do a part-time job without it affecting your life with me.'

'Lots of women work and still manage to run a home—usually without any staff at all.'

'They don't do the amount of entertaining we do.'

'You're making difficulties that don't exist. You don't want your wife to work because of your position.'

'Do you blame me?'

'I certainly do. If I were a doctor you wouldn't expect me to give up my job just because I married you.'

'If you *were* a doctor I wouldn't have married you.'

She stared at him in astonishment. 'You can't mean that!'

His eyes were so pale that they looked opaque, though it might have been a trick of the lamplight. 'I'm not sure,' he said softly, and was prevented from explaining further by the entry of their manservant with a small but exquisite basket of flowers: a group of four tiger lilies on a bed of African violets.

'How fabulous!' she exclaimed, and even before she took out the card knew it was from Roger.

'Both these blooms remind me of you,' he had penned,

'but as I am not sure which is predominant, I am taking no chances!'

Aware of Luke eyeing the basket with disfavour, she mischievously gave him the card and saw him look even more dourly at the offending flowers.

'I never knew Roger was such a wit,' he said. 'Be careful of him, Emily, he isn't a young man to be treated lightly.'

'Are you warning me against him?'

'Is it necessary for me to do so?'

She shrugged. 'Admittedly I don't know him as well as you do, but then I probably see him in a different way.' She looked at Luke frankly. 'I enjoyed his company today; he was amusing and flattering.'

'You sound like a typical woman.'

'I thought you liked typical women. After all, Gina is such an obvious *femme fatale*!'

She had never before made any sarcastic remark about Gina and he gave her a sharp stare. But with a diplomacy that made her admire him and dislike him at one and the same time, he went over to the sideboard and replenished his drink, also changing the subject to tell her the background of the guests who were coming to dinner tonight. Deciding that two could play at the same game, she pretended to give him all her attention, though her mind was busy speculating yet again why he was so reluctant for her to continue seeing Roger.

For his part Luke did not understand his attitude either. All he knew was that he had been irritated at seeing Emily and Roger together in the restaurant. Throughout his meal he had watched them surreptitiously, his irritation turning to anger as he had become aware how much Emily was enjoying herself. She had frequently thrown back her head to laugh: the warm, uninhibited laugh he always associated with her; and when she and Roger had joined him for coffee there had been a sparkle in her eyes which had angered him even more. Yet why shouldn't she enjoy herself in another man's company? On her own admission she had not had much fun in her life, and if finding herself a swan—after

143

being a duckling for so long—had gone slightly to her head, who would have the heart to blame her?

Over the rim of his glass he surveyed her. Emily had never been an ugly duckling, not to anyone with the intelligence to see beneath the dull clothes and badly styled hair. Like the African violets which Roger had sent her, damn his eyes, she possessed a delicate beauty that could flourish unseen if one did not look closely enough. He watched as she went to the window to pull the curtain into place. Her beauty was far from delicate now; exotic was a much better word to describe her creamy white skin and seal-black hair; her great, glowing eyes framed by those startlingly thick straight lashes. Had he been given the choice when he had first met her, she would have been the last girl he would have wanted to marry; which only went to show what a fool he was and how clever it had been of Gina to choose Emily for him.

Unbidden, there flashed into his mind a picture of Gina's face, blank with astonishment at the sight of Emily on her return from Paris. He had seen Emily's change rather as a naturalist would have regarded a moth turning into a butterfly, but Gina's surprise had been different. Thinking about it now he could almost have said there had been anger in it, and fear too. Yet surely Gina knew she had nothing to fear from any other woman? And particularly not Emily. Emily was a child with all her life ahead of her; her future lay with someone like Roger. Darn it, not Roger, he wasn't good enough for her. He frowned, trying to think who, of all the young men he knew, he considered worthy to be her husband. None of them, he decided sourly. Not one of them.

The arrival of his first guest brought him back to the immediate present, though he found himself thinking of Gina again as he watched the pretty way Emily glided around the room, making everyone feel at ease. For someone who had done little if any entertaining before her marriage she had developed it into a fine art, and indeed must have a natural gift for it. Even old Carmichael had unbent

144

with her while his hard-faced wife was actually smiling. He sauntered over to Emily and put his arm around her shoulders. She trembled beneath his touch and he gave her a shake.

'I'm not going to eat you. I just came over to compliment you on getting Mrs. Carmichael to smile.'

Emily looked at him. Her cheeks were flushed and she was still trembling. 'Doesn't she usually smile?'

'Not that I've ever seen. What did you say to her?'

'I can't remember. Something nice, I think.'

He laughed. 'Dear Emily! You always say nice things to people. That's why they like you.'

'I must remember that next time I'm talking to you.'

'I like you whatever you say.'

'Do you?' There was an odd look in her eyes that he could not fathom.

'Of course,' he said in surprised tones. 'Don't you know?' He was annoyed when someone came up to speak to her before she could answer him, and as he turned away to talk to someone else he vowed to resume their conversation when they were alone together.

It was midnight before the final guest left and Emily, still keyed up, went round plumping up the cushions and emptying ashtrays into the waste paper basket.

'Leave it for the maid,' he ordered, 'and sit down and relax.'

'I hate to leave cigarette stubs in the room all night. I'll empty them down the chute.'

'Then come back and talk to me for ten minutes.'

She nodded and, waste paper basket in hand, hurried out. As the door closed the telephone rang, and wondering who could be calling him so late, he lifted the receiver. It was Gina, her voice high and breathless.

'Luke!' she cried. 'It's Charles.' He didn't need her to go on, and though she did, he was only half listening. So it had finally happened, and when least expected.

'I'll be right over,' he said quietly, and was replacing the telephone when Emily came back into the room, her look

145

enquiring. 'It was Gina.' His voice was so low it surprised him, and he cleared his throat. 'Charles had a heart attack earlier this evening. He died half an hour ago.'

'Poor Charles,' Emily whispered. 'If only you'd been there with him.'

'In a way I'm glad I wasn't.'

She looked at him, but he did not explain what he meant: nor was there any need for him to do so. Even in her sorrow she was glad Luke had sufficient integrity to feel guilty. How could he have stayed by Charles's bed and watched him die, knowing that with his death Gina would be free to marry him?

The thought hit her like a physical blow and she caught at the back of a chair.

'I said I would go over to Gina.' Luke was speaking again. 'Do you want to come with me?'

'Why should I?'

'You were—you are her friend.'

'She'll have you to comfort her,' Emily said swiftly. 'She won't need anybody else.'

Luke looked at her for a long moment. 'I'll say good-night, then, Emily. Don't wait up for me; I'm not sure what time I'll be back.'

CHAPTER ELEVEN

EMILY had always known that her marriage to Luke would end when Gina was free, but she had never envisaged it happening so quickly. With Luke gone from the flat she remained wakeful through most of the night, and when dawn came she had still not reached a decision as to what she should do. Logically there was no longer any reason for her to remain here; the sooner their marriage was annulled the better it would be for her. But how empty life would be for her.

'Take a hold of yourself, Emily Adams,' she said aloud, and quickly corrected it to Emily Lamb. For that was the way she must think of herself again. Yet not the same Emily Lamb she had once been. It might be possible to turn back the clock but never, she realised, to the same hour. She would resume her old life, probably even her old job—she had been away from it such a short time that she was sure it was still vacant. Yet it would never be the same as it was.

Pushing aside the bedclothes, she bathed and dressed, and was having breakfast in the dining-room when Luke came in. She saw from his face that he had not had an easy night. He looked strained and tired and there was golden stubble on his chin which softened the hard line of his jaw without darkening it. In an odd way it made him look older and vulnerable; the way he would look when he was an old man. 'I won't be seeing him then,' she thought dully, and felt the sting of tears in her eyes. Quickly she poured a cup of coffee and set it in front of him. He smiled his thanks and sipped it, and it was half empty before he spoke.

'The funeral will be at the end of the week. Quite a lot of people will be flying in from the Continent as well as the States.'

147

'It was very sudden, wasn't it?'

He looked surprised. 'It has been on the cards for the last two years.'

'If you'd thought it imminent you wouldn't have married me,' she said boldly.

'He did show a slight improvement in the past few months,' Luke conceded. 'He had been having a new kind of treatment and was told that if he took things carefully he could go on for years.'

'But now he's dead and everything has changed for you.' Emily did not know why she was mortifying herself in this way. Only that she had an intense desire to know the worst. Not that she did not already know it; she just wanted to hear Luke verbalise it. Instead he set his cup sharply on its saucer and stood up.

'I'm going to shower and change. You appreciate that there will be quite a lot for me to do—arrangements to make.'

'Why can't Roger do it? He was Charles's nephew.'

'Gina would rather I did it. You don't seem to realise what a shock this has been to her.'

'A relief as well, I should think,' Emily said bluntly, and saw Luke's look of disapproval.

'I'm surprised at your lack of sympathy, Emily. Gina was Charles's wife for ten years.'

'She was also involved with you for the last two of them! For heaven's sake spare me any platitudes about bereaved widows!'

'Gina didn't love Charles in a passionate way,' Luke went on as though he had not heard the interruption, 'but as if she were his daughter. If she had met me years ago—before Charles fell ill—she would have been able to leave him. But by the time we did meet, it was too late. The least you can do is to commend her for playing fair with him.'

'I commend her for playing a waiting game,' Emily retorted. 'You're a fool, Luke! Gina didn't stay with Charles because he was ill. She married him for his money and that's the reason she remained with him. If she could have you as a lover into the bargain, so much the better!'

'That's the sort of remark I would expect to hear from one of Gina's enemies, not from her friend.'

'I'm *not* Gina's friend.'

His eyes flashed, more silver now than grey. 'What has happened to your charity, Emily, to your kindness?'

'I don't feel that the situation merits either. You and Gina have finally got what you wanted. You have your position at Harricks and now you can have Charles's wife. She has you and Charles's money. You should both be feeling very pleased with yourselves. At the risk of uttering a truism, I'd say you deserve each other!'

Angrily he turned and swung out of the room, banging the door hard behind him.

Emily did not see Luke again before he left the flat. She had been invited to attend a private viewing at an art gallery, but she did not have the heart to go, and instead put on a tweed coat and went for a walk in Hyde Park. It was the next best thing to walking in the countryside, though she missed the total freedom of empty fields and the complete absence of noise. Here one was always conscious of the hum of traffic and the smell of fumes, and she was suddenly homesick for her own home. Strange, she thought, that despite her marriage, she still thought of the cottage as home. Yet not so strange in view of the fact that she had never allowed herself to think of her marriage as real. How blithely she had considered staying in London and taking on a different career once she parted from Luke. She might have done it, too, if her marriage had lasted longer; but the brief months of its duration had not been long enough to atrophy the nerve ends of her past life. Yes, she would return to the country and her old job. Among friends from the past it would be easier to stop hankering for a future that could never be hers.

Walking back to the flat she knew that diplomacy should be taking her to Gina. But the thought of false commiseration was anathema. How could she sympathise with Gina when she knew that Charles's death—while not actually prayed for—had nonetheless been looked forward to with relief?

Both the heavens and Charles's widow wept at his funeral, though Gina, in mink and black crêpe, her red-gold hair covered by a wisp of chiffon, looked lovelier than the grey, sodden skies. Watching the enormous crowd of mourners, predominantly men, with a smattering of elderly female relatives whom Charles had apparently taken care of for years, Emily was glad that Gina had lived a lie until Charles's death. It was strange that a man who had always been so sensitive to people's feelings had remained unaware that his wife did not love him. Or perhaps, having accepted the fact that she loved him as a father, he had been unable to comprehend that she could love another man with passion. Certainly he had never had any inkling of her relationship with Luke.

Emily's glance slipped to her husband, tall and quiet beside her, his silver-fair hair ruffled slightly by the sharp breeze playing around the graveside. She closed her mind to the sight of it; closed it too to the rest of the scene around her, so that she was startled when her arm was taken by Roger, who guided her past the line of black limousines. Luke, as befitted his position as senior member of Charles's company and the man known to have been nominated by him as his successor, was guiding Gina away from the grave, and she clung to him, a picture of bereaved widowhood.

'Drive back to the house with *me*,' Roger murmured to Emily. 'It looks as if Luke will be driving with Gina.'

Emily nodded, glad not to have to face Charles's relatives or other business acquaintances, and she breathed a sigh of relief as they left the black and white scene behind them and drove towards Mayfair.

'What's going to happen to you now?' Roger asked, his voice loud above the throaty hum of the car. It was a luxurious car, she noticed: a black and silver Porsche, and it made her realise that for all his youth Roger was a wealthy man and likely to be much wealthier now that his uncle was dead.

'What do you mean?' she asked.

'Well you won't be staying with Luke now that Gina's free.'

'I haven't thought that far ahead,' she said stonily.

'It isn't *that* far ahead. It's here and now. You can't run away from the truth, Emily. Anyway, I thought you were a girl who liked to face facts.'

'Not disturbing ones.'

'You are the one who's trying to disturb them. *I'm* trying to put them in order for you.'

'Thanks,' she said bitterly. 'I can do without your help.'

They drove for several minutes in silence and her anger began to abate. What Roger said was true. To deny it was futile. After all, he was only saying to her what she had said to Luke. What would his reaction be if he knew she had received five thousand pounds for becoming Luke's wife, with another five thousand pounds to follow on the day their marriage was annulled? Without giving herself time to think, she told him.

The engine raced beneath Roger's foot. 'I assumed it was something like that, but I'd no idea it was so much. Still, he can afford it; and he'll get it back a thousandfold now.'

'You might not like Luke,' she protested, 'but you can't believe he wants to marry Gina for her money or encouraged her to remain with Charles because of it.'

'He won't be needing Gina's money,' Roger said, answering only half the question. 'Being with Harricks has given him enough of his own. And now he will be the chairman too. Yes, marrying you was a clever move.'

'You engineered it,' she reminded him. 'You deserve some of the credit!'

'I never thought he would get married,' Roger said frankly. 'Gina has been the only woman in his life for two years.'

'Did you hope he would resign and leave you to step into his shoes?'

'I'm not going to take offence at that remark,' Roger said calmly, 'because I know you're upset and angry. But I had no desire, at any time, to step into Luke's shoes—either in business or in his personal life.' He slowed the car and regarded her for a brief moment. 'But I do want to step into his shoes now. I'm making no bones about it. I love you, and I want to marry you.'

'Don't!' she burst out. 'You make it sound as if you're glad Charles is dead; as if his dying was the best thing that could have happened.'

'That's what Gina feels,' he said. 'But you know very well I loved my uncle. The only reason I feel relieved about his death is because I've always been afraid he might have discovered what a bitch he'd married!' Once more he slowed the car and glanced at her. 'If you believe that.'

It was difficult to deny his sincerity and she sighed and nodded, at the same time glad to see they had reached Charles's house. Gina's house now, she thought, as she gave her coat to the butler. She had no intention of going up-stairs to leave it in Gina's room—those days were over— and followed Roger into the drawing-room where a buffet table had been set out and several servants, hired for the occasion, were dispensing drinks and food. She shivered, wishing she didn't have to face another hour of forced conversation.

'When am I going to see you again?' Roger asked pleadingly.

She was about to reply when Luke and Gina came in. Even in pseudo-grief she looked beautiful. She had divested herself of her hat and coat, and her simple black dress clung to every line of her tall, graceful figure. She held on to Luke's arm and he was forced to move around beside her as she went from group to group. Did other people realise what a wonderful couple they made, Emily wondered bitterly, and was Gina deliberately giving indication that this was the way it was going to be in the future? How soon would she want to marry Luke? Would she obey convention and wait for a year or would she ignore

152

what people might say and marry Luke the moment he was free? Either way it didn't matter, Emily knew, for she had no intention of standing by to wait while Luke and Gina decided how to play their cards. She had helped them to deal the hand, but she was darned if she was going to wait for the game to be played out.

She swung round to Roger. 'Will you drive me home? My own home,' she amended, 'in the country.'

He was startled, but nodded. 'When do you want to leave?'

'In a few moments. But let's be unobtrusive about it. When you see me slip out, follow me.'

'I might not see you if I get involved in conversation.' Roger's narrow face was unexpectedly tender as he stared down at Emily, who seemed particularly small and fragile in black. 'Let's meet in fifteen minutes at my car.'

'Fine.'

She was glad to have made a firm arrangement with him, for he was almost immediately whisked away by an elderly man who spoke with a heavy French accent. The drawing-room was so full of people that she had lost sight of Gina and Luke, and she began to edge to the door. All the directors of Harrick Investments were there with their wives, and since most of them knew her and were glad to take the opportunity of seeing her again, her progress was inevitably slowed down. But at last she escaped into the hall and hurried to the powder room where the women's coats were usually placed when Gina gave a party. But there were no coats there today, and quickly she ran up to Gina's bedroom. A metal rail had been placed against one wall and it was choc-à-bloc with an assortment of furs and tweeds. She searched out her own coat, a lustrous black velvet one.

'It reminded me of your hair,' Luke had said when it had arrived unexpectedly from Harrods, and she had confronted him with it. 'I hope it's the right size,' he had added. 'I had to guess it.'

She slipped the coat on, trying to push away any more

153

thoughts of Luke; knowing how impossibly difficult it was going to be while she was still surrounded by everything that reminded her of him. She bent to pick up her handbag and as she did so, saw Gina and Luke come in. Instantly Emily remembered the last time she had been in Gina's bedroom. Luke had been here too, and it was her entry during their passionate embrace that had told her the truth of their relationship. But none of this showed in her face, which remained devoid of expression.

'I'm just leaving,' she told them, 'so you'll be quite undisturbed.'

'We don't have to worry about that any more,' Gina said softly. 'Luke only came up to get a letter Charles had left for him.' She glided over to the dressing table and took out an envelope from the top drawer. She handed it to Luke and he hesitated and then quickly slit it open and extracted a single sheet of writing paper. It took him a moment to read, and watching him, Emily saw his face flush and his lids blink rapidly.

'It's just a personal goodbye from him,' he said huskily, refolding the paper.

Gina moved closer towards him. 'Did he say anything in it about it?'

'Only that he hopes I will—that I should take care of you.'

'Then he never knew.' There was immense satisfaction in Gina's voice and she sank on to the bed, her skirts fluttering around her like a dark cobweb. 'Oh, Luke, I'm so glad we did what we knew to be right. We would never have known real happiness if we had been responsible for his death. But this way we can be happy without feeling any guilt at all.'

'Please excuse me,' Emily said loudly, and went to the door.

'Wait!' Gina called. 'We've things to discuss.'

'You don't need me here for that.'

'But we do. You're still Luke's wife and we must decide how best to end it.'

'Can't that wait for the moment?' Luke continued.

154

'What is there to wait for?' Gina demanded. 'Your reason for marrying Emily is over. The quicker you're free the better.'

Emily shivered at the bluntness of the words. Here now was the answer to the question she had asked herself downstairs. Gina intended to ignore convention and acknowledge her love for Luke the moment she could do so.

'Gina, please,' he protested. 'Let's discuss it another time.'

'Don't be silly, darling.' Gina focused on Emily. 'It's silly for us to pretend, don't you think? You're very lucky to be free so soon. It must be the easiest ten thousand pounds you'll ever earn in your life!'

'For heaven's sake, Gina!' Luke cried. 'There's no need to be rude.'

'Since when do you regard honesty as rudeness?' Gina said with an amused laugh. 'And I'm sure Emily appreciates honesty.'

'Maybe she does,' Luke replied. 'But there's no need to have this discussion here and now. Let it wait for——'

'There's no point in waiting,' Emily interrupted. 'The quicker I'm shot of both of you, the better!' She swung round on Gina. 'It might be your ambition to become Mrs. Luke Adams as quickly as possible, but I'm just as eager to give up that title.' She wrenched open the door and ran into the corridor, wondering fleetingly if Luke would come after her, yet feeling no surprise when he didn't.

Luke watched Emily go with an emotion he could not fathom; it was too new, too strange; all he did know was that he was furious with Gina.

'Did you have to talk to Emily like that?' he asked closing the door and coming further into the bedroom.

'What was wrong with what I said? She's been expecting to hear it.' The blue eyes were reproachful. 'I'm surprised *you* hadn't said it to her already.'

'With Charles just dead?' Luke shook his head. He had occasionally been confronted by the icy determination that many women seemed able to display when they wanted something, but it was a trait he had never expected to find in Gina. She had always been so gentle and soft. He tried and failed to close his mind to the matter-of-fact way she had been able to face the future; giving no thought to the man whom she had only just laid to rest; a man who had been her devoted husband for ten years; whose love she had accepted and whose money she now— He stopped, horrified at where his thoughts had taken him. Blast Emily and her insidious tongue! Yet her comments about Gina refused to be forgotten, and like a geyser, everything she had said gushed forth into his mind.

'It would have been more diplomatic if you had allowed *me* to speak to Emily,' he said aloud.

'Since when do I have to be careful with her?' Gina came towards him. 'I'm free and I want to be with you. Oh, Luke, don't you know what this means to us? We needn't pretend any more. We needn't hide our love.' She went to put her arms around him, but he moved slightly, unconsciously, and only realised he had done so as he saw her hands drop to her sides.

'I never wanted to hide our love,' he replied. 'You were the one who wanted to do that.'

'You know why.'

'When I asked you to come away with me the first time, Charles wasn't ill. At least not so ill that he would have died.'

Gina's delicate features sharpened. 'Why are we talking about the past? We should be thinking of the future.'

'Then we must think of it carefully.' Luke heard himself speak and felt he was listening to a stranger. Why did he feel as if his emotions were encased in glass? As if he was seeing Gina through a mist? But it was not a mist, that was the wrong word. It was as if he were seeing her clearly for the first time, and she was blurred now only because this new image of her was out of focus with the image he had always carried in his heart. He stared at her classically oval face; at the smooth skin, the delicately sculptured bones, the large blue eyes that were watching him soulfully. She was the most beautiful woman he had ever seen. Even looking at her dispassionately could not detract from that. Yet there was something empty in the loveliness; an arid quality that prevented the beauty from taking on warmth. He put a hand to his forehead, surprised to find his skin was damp.

'Are you ill, Luke?' Gina came closer to him, her perfume making his senses swim the way it always did.

'I have a headache,' he murmured. 'I haven't eaten since breakfast.'

'Oh, darling.' She put her arms around him. 'People should be starting to go soon, then I'll order a meal for you. Or would you like to have it now, up here?'

'No, thanks. I don't want anything to eat.' He moved back a step, but Gina's arms remained around him and automatically his hands came up to hold her. She gave a small sigh and relaxed against him. Her head fitted perfectly into the hollow of his shoulder and she gave another murmur of contentment.

'I feel so right with you,' she whispered. 'I love you so much.'

Luke rested his cheek on the red-gold head, feeling the hair rubbing against his skin like a swatch of silk. How many times had he dreamed of the moment when he could hold Gina in his arms and know there was no other man to come between them. Yet though Charles had gone, Emily had taken his place, and now she had come between him and Gina.

'We can't stay up here any longer,' he said quietly, and disengaged Gina's arms from around his neck. 'We must go downstairs or everyone will be wondering where we are.'

'They'll think I wasn't feeling well and that you came up to sit with me.'

She put her arms around his neck again and pulled his head down until his mouth lay upon hers. Her body pressed close to his and her breasts moved and swelled against his chest. It had been several weeks since he had held Gina close, so that he was disconcerted by his lack of response

157

and wondered if he could be ill, or if pressure of other work had tired him. Certainly he could never remember a time when he had held Gina in his arms and not wanted to make love to her. Gently he disengaged himself from her hold.

'We must go downstairs.'

With grace she accepted his command and walked beside him along the corridor. He knew they made a striking couple; knew too that had he not been so recently married, many of the people in the drawing-room would have started to pair them together. Perhaps some already did. He and Gina had been able to fool Charles, possibly because Charles had wanted to be fooled, but others would have been able to judge the situation through unblinkered eyes, as Roger had done.

'I want to go home and talk to Emily,' he murmured as they reached the hall.

'Will you come back this evening?'

He hesitated and then shrugged, unwilling to make a definite commitment. He could not fathom his reason and it became more obscure the more he tried to analyse it as he drove through the crowded rush-hour streets to Park Lane. Entering his flat, he stopped in surprise as he saw the pile of luggage. Who on earth had come to stay with them? There were four cases in all; new and expensive and initialled in black and gold. He looked closer at the initials, his surprise changing to disbelief and then sudden anger. How dared Emily think she could walk out on him like this!

'Emily,' he called, 'where are you?'

There was no answer and he strode down the hall to the guest suite at the far end. Even as he pushed open the door he realised it was the first time he had been in here, and the thought struck him as ironic.

Emily was bent over a case on the bed and she looked up as he came in.

'Why didn't you answer me?' he demanded.

She shrugged and went on packing, meticulously folding

wisps of silk and lace.

'Leave those things,' he said harshly, and striding over banged the case shut, narrowly avoiding her fingers. 'Leave it,' he repeated, 'and answer me!'

'I've nothing to say.'

'Do you mind telling me what you're doing?'

'I should have thought it was obvious. I'm obeying Gina's orders and leaving you.'

'Gina can't give you orders.'

'Tell her that, not me.'

'I'm telling *you*,' he said harshly, 'because you seem to be under the misapprehension that you have to obey them.'

The look she gave him was wary, as if she was not sure what he meant. Yet how could she know when he didn't know himself?

'The reason we were married no longer exists.' Emily was speaking again and he forced himself to listen, wondering for the second time within an hour what was wrong with him. Only a short while ago he had had the feeling he was seeing Gina for the first time, and now he was experiencing the same thing with Emily. He closed and opened his eyes. It was even more strange than that, for he wasn't just seeing one Emily but a hundred different images of her, each one melding into another until he felt himself to be the centre of a whirling kaleidoscope. Emily on the day he married her. Emily in Paris, walking towards him across the restaurant, her dark hair gleaming, her face alight with humour. Emily smiling and then pensive; critical and sympathetic; intelligent one moment, perversely female and argumentative the next.

Vividly he remembered their brief but happy stay in Paris when, for some inexplicable reason, he had felt free and younger than he had felt for years; light-hearted too, as if his honeymoon had been a genuine one and Emily was the wife he had wanted to share it with. He had felt he had grown to know her during those days, but the knowing had faded in the months since their return, so that she was now almost a stranger to him. Yet not quite a stranger, for he could still remember how it had felt when he had kissed her. It had been like holding a bird: a gently quivering creature that he had been afraid to hold too tightly lest he crush it.

'Gina's right, Luke.' Emily was speaking again. 'There's no longer any reason for us to remain married. The sooner we get it annulled the better.'

'What will you do?' he asked.

'I still have my cottage and I'm sure I can get my job back.'

'You seem very anxious to leave me.'

'I have my own life to lead, too.'

The door behind Luke opened, and Roger's voice said: 'Shall I take the luggage downstairs, Emily?'

'What the hell!' Luke swung round to look at the younger man. 'Who gave you the right to take Emily away?' Only as he saw the look of comical surprise on Roger's face did Luke realise the ludicrousness of his question, and with an enormous effort of will, he forced himself to speak in a passable imitation of his normal soft-spoken manner. 'If Emily decides she wants to leave here, Roger, I'm perfectly capable of taking her wherever she wishes to go. I suggest you say goodbye and get out.'

Roger looked past him to Emily who was still standing by the bed. Luke knew she must have nodded, for Roger looked back at him and shrugged. 'Emily wanted to go back to the country and I offered to drive her.'

'Quite the boy scout, aren't you?' Luke deliberately put amusement into his voice, glad to see it did the trick and that Roger flushed.

'Emily's life has been singularly lacking in boy scouts until now,' Roger replied. 'But I'm more than willing to make up for the deficiency.'

'Be careful what you say, old chap,' Luke said quietly, 'or I shall start to give *you* an ultimatum.'

Roger paled and then spoke directly to Emily. 'You know where to find me if you want me.'

'Yes, Roger,' her voice was breathless. 'But you'd better

go. I'll see you to the door.' She took a step forward, but Luke's arm barred her way.

'Roger can find his own way out,' he said softly. 'Goodbye, Roger,' he said without turning. 'I'll see you in the office tomorrow.' Not until the front door slammed did Luke speak again. 'Sit down, Emily. It's been a trying day for you.'

Gently he shepherded her to a chair and pushed her into it. The bones of her shoulders felt tiny beneath his hands and he had to restrain the urge to curve his fingers round them. She curled into the back of the seat and tilted her head to look at him. Her eyes did not have the softness of Gina's but gazed at him fearlessly and with contempt. But why shouldn't they hold contempt when he had done nothing to deserve anything else from her?

Their brief life together flashed through his mind: the unsavoury reason for their marriage and the more unsavoury reason for the annulment of it; to say nothing of the events that lay between. The evenings he had spent with Gina when Emily had been left here alone; the dinner parties where she had acted as his hostess and he had treated her as if she had been professionally paid to do it. Her efficient running of his home; her availability when he had wanted someone to talk to—and how bright and perceptive she always was—and her ability to melt into the background if she felt she was not required.

He had taken all this for granted; worse, he had considered it his right to do so. Yet alongside this another feeling had grown: subtly, stealthily it had caught up on him. But like a fool he had been too blind to see it. He clenched his hands at his sides. Too blinded by the past to know when that past was dead. But he knew it now; knew also, with dreadful clarity, that unless he could convince Emily that the past was dead, his future would be dead too.

I love her. The words came into his mind so simply and gently that it was like water lapping on a sandy shore. And with the same insidiousness it permeated his consciousness, turning his entire being into a void that only she could fill.

It was not the burning idolatrous passion he had known for Gina, but something richer and more varied; compounded of desire and laughter, of understanding and compassion; something—he knew with terrible desolation—that would be with him for the rest of his life.

Carefully he sat down opposite to her. He had to talk to her, but he didn't know where to begin. How could he tell her he loved her and expect her to believe him when all his actions had pointed to the opposite? No, he dared not admit his feelings yet; he must bide his time and show her without words. He thought of Roger's eagerness to drive her away from him and knew a violent longing to smash his fists into the young man's face. No one was going to take Emily away from him. Emily of the great heart and gentle manner; who was the size of a starling but had the courage of an eagle.

'Why are you looking at me like that?' she burst out.

He blinked. 'Like what?'

'As if I'm a stranger.'

'You are. We are all strangers to each other.'

'Don't be maudlin,' she said with asperity. 'It doesn't become you.'

'Back on form again, I see.'

She nodded, and her body moved, making him notice that her feet did not reach the ground. Sitting docilely in the big chair she reminded him of a little girl. As if aware of his thoughts she slid forward in the seat until her delicately arched feet touched the carpet. His eyes moved up her slender legs to the rounded curve of her hips and he amended his earlier thought. Not a little girl; very much a woman. The stirring in his body left him in no doubt and he had to firmly restrain himself from going over and pulling her into his arms.

'If you don't want Roger to drive me to my home,' she continued, 'perhaps you'll let the chauffeur take me.'

'*This* is your home,' he said. 'You can't leave now. We've only been married a couple of months.'

'I don't expect you to pay me the other five thousand

162

pounds,' she said, and confounded him into silence. 'I realise you expected me to—to act the part of your wife for a
much longer period. To pay me such a large amount for
such a short time is—is unnecessary. So if we could just
leave things the way they are and——'

'Money is the last thing in the world I'm thinking of,' he
interrupted.

'Then are you worried at what people will say if I leave
you so soon after becoming your wife?'

She had given him the lead he wanted, and he took it.
'Since the whole purpose of our marriage was to avoid any
gossip about myself and Gina, it would rather spoil the
effect if we rushed into each other's arms the second
Charles is dead.'

'Gina asked me to go immediately.'

He longed to say he didn't give a damn what Gina
wanted, and forcibly held himself in check. So many things
were becoming clear to him that he knew how a blind man
must feel when he was unexpectedly given back his sight.
Was this why Gina had not wanted him to leave the company and try to make another life for himself? Had she
feared that if he were away from her he would see her for
what she was; a spoilt and selfish beauty who wanted to
have her cake and to eat it too? He glanced at Emily and
knew that no matter where he was and with whom he
worked, this black-haired creature of flame and fire would
always haunt him.

'Gina wants me to go,' Emily repeated.

'She wasn't thinking clearly,' he replied. 'Once she does
she will agree that my idea is the best.'

'I can't stay here with you.' Emily jumped to her feet
and went to the bed to resume her packing. 'You needn't
start the annulment yet if you don't want to, but I think it
would be better if I went back to my own home.'

'I won't let you.' Luke's voice was harsher than he had
intended, and he saw the doubt on her face as she turned to
look at him. 'We made a bargain,' he went on, 'and I insist
you stick to it.'

163

'You can't—not if I'm willing to forgo the other five thousand pounds.'

'I'm not prepared to let you forgo it, and unless I agree to alter our agreement, it still stands. Of course, if you insist on breaking it——'

'I do,' she said quickly.

'Then you must return the first five thousand pounds.'

Her look of hope changed to anger. 'You know I can't give you back the money. I gave it to Clive.'

'Ah, yes.' Mention of Clive gave Luke another stab of jealousy and, unaccustomed to such an emotion, he said the first thing that came into his head. 'Does Roger know about Clive, or does he think he's the first love of your life?'

'You know I'm not in love with Roger,' she said crossly. 'I like him, but that's all.'

'He intends to change that,' Luke said, so delighted by her reply that he wanted to shout for joy.

'He might succeed in doing so.'

Emily's calm retort caused the joy to subside as quickly as it had arisen, and he wondered whether she was being deliberately irritating. But then she did not know he loved her, so why would she try to hurt him?

'You don't really mean what you said about my having to repay the money, do you, Luke?' She was leaning against the bed, almost as if she needed its support, and he had to harden his heart against her, knowing that unless he did she would be able to do what she wanted with him. And he dared not let her go back to her cottage. What chance would he have of making her love him if they were miles apart? Besides, if he went down to see her she would probably slam the door in his face.

'I want you to stay here,' he insisted, 'for six months at least. After that you may go.'

She turned her back on him. 'Very well. If you insist, I have no choice.'

Across the room Luke watched her, then because he found her proximity too disturbing he went to the door. He

164

had his hand on the knob when her voice made him pause.

'If you want me to stay here in order to hoodwink your associates for a few more months, then I'll expect you to play your part.'

'Haven't I always?'

'Not quite. Now that Gina is an eligible widow I suggest you curtail your dinners *à deux*.'

For a joyous instant he wondered if she were jealous, but her next words disabused him.

'Since you're preventing me from enjoying my life for the next six months, I think I'm entitled to do the same to you.'

'Of course,' he replied, and walked out before she could see the pleasure in his eyes. Six months with Emily. If that didn't give him a chance to show her how much he loved her and to make her love him, then nothing would.

CHAPTER TWELVE

EMILY sat in front of the fire and covertly watched Luke who was sitting opposite her. Rain pattered on the windows, but the stormy night was hidden by the heavy silk drapes that had been drawn across them. It was hard to believe that two months had passed since Charles had died, and harder still to realise how happy she had been with Luke ever since. That this was due to a subtle change in his attitude to her, she had no doubt, for though difficult to define in words, it was nonetheless tangible. He was less restless too, and in the evenings after dinner, when they were not giving a party or going to one, he was content to sit with her and work on papers or read. Frequently they listened to music and occasionally watched television. It was almost as if they were a genuinely happy couple, and anyone watching them during one such evening at home might have been forgiven for thinking that they were.

The docile way he had complied with her request not to see Gina had also come as a surprise. They occasionally encountered her when they went to dine with other people, but whether Gina was there at Luke's behest or in her own right, Emily did not know and knew better than to ask, deciding it was wiser to be content with the knowledge that Gina did not come to their flat. But this, she recognised, must end soon, for if they were continuing their marriage in order to quieten gossip, it would only arouse it if Gina was never invited to their home. Many times when the phone rang and she picked it up, she expected to hear her husky voice at the other end, but as the weeks had become one month and then two, she had decided that Luke must have told Gina of the promise he had been forced to make. What had her reaction been to it? Obviously she must have agreed with Luke's determination to avoid gossip, and on the day of the funeral had obviously been too overwrought to think clearly about it.

Behind her the record of a Mozart Horn Concerto came to an end and both she and Luke rose simultaneously to put on another one.

'Let's have something light,' Luke suggested, rummaging through the records.

'You don't have any light music.'

'Nothing?'

'A few old Crosbys that I couldn't possibly bear to hear.'

'What do *you* call light?' he smiled.

'I call it a load of rubbish!'

His smile turned to laughter. 'After such a forthright reply I dare not make a choice. You decide what you want to hear.'

'Nothing for the moment. I'd like to talk to you.'

Silently he sat down again and she marvelled, as she always did, at his aura of quietness. Only on two occasions could she remember him losing his control: the evening of Charles's funeral and the night in their hotel suite in Paris when he had held her in his arms. Hurriedly she began to speak.

'I think we should invite Gina to dinner,' she said, and knew from his expression she had surprised him.

'Are you sure? The last time you spoke about her you——'

'I was in a temper,' she finished for him. 'You had forced me to go on with this charade and I wanted to hurt you.'

'And now you don't?'

She shrugged, the mannerism neatly avoiding a verbal reply. 'I've made out a list of people to whom we owe dinner invitations, and Gina fits in well with them.' She handed him a slip of paper and he glanced through the names.

'Why don't we ask Lord Edgeworth too?' he suggested. 'He's highly eligible and it might be a good idea to have him along here.'

'You don't need to carry your pretence that far,' she said icily. 'The act you're putting on at the moment is quite good enough.'

Luke pulled at his lip and she had the impression he wanted to say more but was holding himself in check. She bit back a sigh and hoped she had the strength of mind to carry on like this for the next four months.

'Are *you* finding it hard to put on an act?' he asked unexpectedly.

His question took her by surprise but she did not lose command of herself. 'It isn't easy,' she confessed. 'I know you've asked me to stay with you, but I also know how much you hate having me here.'

'That isn't true. I——'

The telephone cut him short and with an exclamation he answered it. A few clipped words later he passed it across to her. 'The boy scout,' he said sarcastically, but made no move to leave the room as she took the call.

Conscious of Luke's presence, she was aware of sounding stilted, but this did not prevent her from accepting Roger's invitation to lunch with him the next day.

'How often do you see him?' Luke asked as she settled back in her chair.

'Once a week.'

'How often does he call you?'

'Why?'

'I'm entitled to know.'

'I don't remember that playing the jealous husband was part of our bargain; or is it an added refinement of your own?'

'Don't make me lose my temper,' he snapped.

'Then don't make me lose mine!' Annoyed because his anger moved her to tears, she was intent on hurting him. 'You've forced me to stay with you for another six months, Luke, but there was nothing in our arrangement to say I wasn't to fall in love with anyone else.'

'*Have* you fallen in love?' he demanded.

'It's none of your business!'

'Oh yes, it is.' He reached out and yanked her to her feet. His hands were like iron weights on her shoulders and she would have crumpled at the knees had he not been supporting her. 'Answer me!' he grated. 'Have you fallen in love with Roger?'

'Yes, I have!' she cried. 'And there's nothing you can do about it.'

'We'll see about that!' With each word he gave her a violent shake. 'You're not to go out with him any more. Do you understand me?'

'I'll go out with him whenever I like!'

'If you do, I'll follow you and drag you back here!'

'You wouldn't dare.'

'Try me,' he said, and there was a wildness in his eyes that exhilarated her.

'Threats,' she taunted. 'That's all you're capable of.'

'I'll give you action, then!' he muttered, and jerked her so roughly against him that the breath was crushed from her body.

His mouth fastened on hers, warm and demanding, and she tried to struggle free of him. But her strength was puny against the hard barrier of his arms and the pressure of his mouth increased. He bent her backwards and she would have lost her balance had he not been holding her tightly. As her feet left the ground she cried out, and he gathered her closer still. Without knowing how, she found herself on the settee with his full weight upon her, making it impossible for her to move. Not that she wanted him to move, for her body was beginning to play her false, telling her one thing while her brain was telling her another. She wanted him to possess her; she wanted to give him her love even though she knew he would never love her in return.

'Emily,' he whispered, and rained little kisses along her cheek.

His mouth came to rest on the shadowed curve between her breasts and his hands caressed them. His touch was like fire and her desire for him was so great that she trembled and clung to him. Yet a remnant of pride refused to let her submit totally, and in the recesses of her mind the name Gina burned, corrosive as acid. There was no love in Luke's

169

need of her: only a physical desire which any woman could have satisfied. Sickened by the knowledge, she pummelled her hands against his chest.

'Let me go!' she cried. 'I'm no substitute for Gina.'

'Emily, don't.'

'You needn't worry,' she taunted. 'Emily won't! Now let me go.'

With an exclamation he drew back, and swift as a faun she was on her feet and at the door. 'If you find it so hard to manage without Gina, you'd better make arrangements to see her. I'd rather you did that than expect me to act as her replacement!'

'That's the last thing I want you to be. Emily, please . . .' He was on his feet and coming towards her. She shook her head vehemently.

'Keep away from me, Luke. If you don't, I'll walk out and put paid to our bargain.'

He stopped moving. 'Do you hate me as much as that?'

She appeared to consider the question, then gave a shake of her head. 'I feel nothing for you, Luke. Nothing.'

Quickly she went out and, with the door closed behind her, leaned for a moment on it, afraid that if she moved away from its support she would fall down. But a sound behind her frightened her into thinking Luke was coming out, and with a stifled cry she ran to her room and locked her door. So far she had managed to hide her love for Luke, but if he touched her again she knew she would give herself away. And she must not do that. If she did, it would make it impossible for her to forget him. Her tears fell fast and she sank on to the bed and buried her face in her pillow.

Alone in the living-room Luke paced the floor, furious with himself for having lost his temper and his control. But anger had flamed his passion into life, breaking the rigid discipline he had exercised over his emotions in the last few months. But it was a discipline he had to continue exercising; if he did not, Emily would leave him.

Throughout the long hours of the night he lay sleepless, with a dull throb above his eyes that developed into a raging headache by morning. It did not improve his mood to enter the dining-room and find Emily at the table looking as composed as she always did, a painful indication that she had given no more thought to him once they had parted. As always when he was with her, the urge to touch her was overwhelming. He longed to feel her delicate bones beneath his fingers; to put his arm around her waist and hold her close to him, where she belonged. The trouble was she did not feel she belonged there at all, and had made it painfully clear that she was counting the days until she could walk out of his life. To envisage her doing this was anguish, and for the thousandth time he wondered what she would say if he told her he loved her. He had been nearer to doing so last night than at any time since he had first discovered it, and if Roger's telephone call had not come when it had, he would have done so. Again he cursed himself for having lost his temper and said things that had been guaranteed to make his high-spirited Emily lose hers. How defiantly she had rounded on him when he had ordered her not to see Roger again, and how successfully her retort had scotched his hopes. She loved Roger. The knowledge was bitter, but he tried not to let it embitter him towards the young man himself. Yet with all the will in the world he believed that he alone could make Emily happy.

'Emily,' he said aloud, and stopped, for she had spoken at exactly the same time and he inclined his head for her to speak first.

'I just wanted to let you know I'm planning to have lunch with Roger—as arranged.'

'I gathered you would,' he said, 'but you've nothing to worry about. I won't break up your loving duet.' He crumpled his napkin and stood up. 'Don't wait dinner for me tonight. I'll be late.'

On his way down to the car he found he was shaking, and he cursed himself for being a fool. He was crazy to let his desire for a slip of a girl take such a hold over him. He forced himself to remember how much he had loved Gina a couple of years ago, and to make himself believe that what

171

he felt for Emily would fade in the same way. But he knew this was untrue; what he felt for Emily was a more encompassing love : one compounded of affection as well as passion. He had grown to like her, to appreciate her mind and personality long before he had grown to love her. Strange that he didn't know exactly when that love had begun. It seemed as if his need of her had always been there. She was the only woman whose integrity he respected. Even at the height of his passion for Gina he would never have trusted her in the same way he would trust Emily. Emily ... He murmured her name as if it were a benediction, and felt a momentary peace enter his mind. He could not allow her to go out of his life; he would fight for her no matter whether she was in love with a hundred other men!

He reached his car and climbed into the back. It drew away from the kerb and he settled against the seat and tried to concentrate on his first appointment. But all he could think of was the mess he had made of his life.

'Did you say something, sir?' his chauffeur asked. 'I didn't quite catch it.'

'Nothing,' Luke muttered. 'I was thinking aloud.'

Thinking. That was all he had done for months, and it had got him nowhere. His row with Emily last night had shown him that. When he had insisted she remain with him for another six months he had hoped that during this time their relationship would develop sufficiently for him to tell her he loved her. But two months of this precious time had gone by with nothing to show for it except her increasing bitterness. He had to do something, but he was darned if he knew what.

A slim woman crossed the road in front of the car, her reddish-brown hair glinting in the sunshine. It reminded him of Gina and instantly he knew the first thing that had to be done. Tell her he no longer loved her. Only then would he be free to go to Emily. He frowned at the thought of how badly Gina would take his confession and cursed his folly for not having told her the truth weeks ago. But they had not met alone since the funeral, for Charles's sister had

172

come from Canada for it and had stayed on in the house until last week, making it difficult for Gina to be her own mistress and also, he thought gratefully, to spend any time with him. The idea of making love to her filled him with shame, the more so because he now saw his behaviour through Emily's eyes. The only good thing he could say about his love affair was that Gina had made the first move towards him. Unfortunately this did not eradicate his guilt; all it did was to make it more bearable.

Arriving at his office he immediately telephoned Gina to ask if she were free to see him that evening.

'I'll make myself free,' she said at once.

'Don't cancel anything on my behalf,' he said quickly. 'I'll only be staying a short while.'

'Don't be silly, darling. Joan isn't here any more. I'll expect you to dinner.'

'Very well,' he said, and pretended that the entry of his secretary made it necessary to end their conversation.

On and off during the day he considered how best to tell Gina the truth. The prospect was daunting and he would rather have faced an irate board of Directors ten times over. Any woman other than Gina would already have guessed from his behaviour in the last few months that he no longer loved her. But she had been so spoiled by men during her life that she could not envisage her charm ever ceasing to hold its appeal. She no doubt saw their infrequent meeting as part of his plan to maintain the correct status of her recent widowhood. This knowledge made him feel worse. How fervently he declared his love for her; how frequently maintained its depth. Yet here he was, coming to tell her it was all over.

What would have happened if she had come away with him when he had first begged her to do so—before Charles's failing health had given her a reason to refuse? Would his love for her have stood the test or would close proximity have destroyed it even sooner? Certainly there would have been no need for a false marriage—which had brought Emily into his life. And had he not met Emily ...

He clenched his fists and thumped them on his desk. Like a callow youth he had mistaken desire for love; had allowed a woman's expertise at lovemaking to blind him to her true character—and also to his own. Disgust swelled his throat and nausea gripped him. What a fool he had been! What a crass, unmitigated fool.

By six o'clock he was in such a state of nerves that he was in two minds whether or not to call Gina and say he was tied up. Yet he had to tell her the truth, and the sooner the better. He remained working in his office until the rush-hour traffic had ceased, then, having dismissed his chauffeur, he drove himself through the rain-swept streets. Drawing up outside the house in Mayfair, he again took hold of his courage, and though he chided himself for being a coward, knew that most men in a similar position would be feeling exactly the same way.

It made matters worse to have Gina greet him with her usual affection, one which she generally reserved for when they were alone. But tonight she had no inhibition about displaying her feelings in front of the elderly butler who was waiting to take his coat.

'Dearest Luke! It's weeks since I've seen you.'

'One week only. You were at the Robinsons' last Tuesday.'

'I don't count that. I mean it's ages since we've been alone together.'

She linked her arm through his and drew him into the drawing-room. She was still wearing black, but it was so décolleté that one was mainly conscious of her pearly skin. Looking at her dispassionately he had to admit there had been nothing wrong with his taste in desiring her; it was his judgment of himself which had been at fault. He should have had sense enough to know that physical attraction would diminish for him unless it was accompanied by mental stimulus, and though Gina was no fool, her mind lacked the breadth and sharpness of true intelligence. Again he was overcome by self-loathing.

'How is Emily?' Gina asked, gliding over to him with a

174

glass of champagne. 'I still can't see why you wanted her to stay with you. I know you did it for my sake, but honestly I don't care what people say about us. We were blameless during Charles's lifetime and now we're entitled to take our happiness.'

'Some people would hardly call us blameless,' he remarked.

'Charles was happy with me until the day he died,' she said firmly. 'I have no sense of guilt whatever.'

'I wish I could say the same.'

The blue eyes narrowed. 'You have no reason to feel guilty.'

'Haven't I? Do you think it was easy for me to work for Charles and at the same time make love to his wife?'

'I wasn't Charles's wife for years. You took nothing from him in that sense. I gave him all he was capable of wanting —and that was companionship and my affection.' She set her glass down and perched on the arm of his chair. 'Darling Luke, stop thinking about the past. It's over.'

Here was the opportunity he wanted. He opened his mouth, but no words came out. Jumping to his feet he went to stand by the mantelpiece. He had faced the Monopolies Commission four days ago with far less inhibition than he was now facing Gina. 'What are your plans?' he asked jerkily.

'My plans?'

'Yes. Now that Charles is dead, what are you going to do?'

'I think that's something we should discuss together. For example, the house. It would be more convenient for us to live here than for me to move into your flat.'

'Do you think we should?' he burst out, and swung round to look at her.

'I don't see why not. But if you would prefer another house then——'

'I mean our marriage,' he intervened, and waited for his words to penetrate. They did so more quickly than he would have credited; so quickly indeed that he wondered whether she had guessed they were coming. Perhaps his aloofness with her since Charles's death had given her a warning after all.

'Are you saying you don't want to marry me?' she asked, her voice huskier than usual.

'I don't think we're right for each other.'

'Spare me that! We were perfectly right for each other until a couple of months ago. Or did you only want me when I was unattainable?'

'You were never unattainable,' he reminded her.

'That's a foul thing to say!'

He felt a swine but stood his ground. 'It's the truth,' he said quietly. 'And truth is the only thing I can offer you. I don't love you, Gina. It has nothing to do with Charles's death. If you think about it you will realise that we haven't seen all that much of each other since my marriage.'

'I assumed you were being careful. I didn't think it was for any other reason.' She shifted her position and the light fell fully on her face. He noticed the bright spots of rouge on her cheeks: the only sign she gave of having lost her natural colour.

'I seem to have been singularly stupid, haven't I, Luke?' Her voice was still quiet, still gentle. 'I know you haven't made love to me since Charles died, but I thought it was because you ... I felt you were paying a last respect to him.'

'After the way I deceived him when he was alive!' Luke gave a hollow laugh. 'When I think of what we did ... the way we acted ...'

'Darling, stop it.' She moved swiftly to his side. 'You're suffering from a bad attack of conscience. It's making you say things you don't mean.'

'I do mean them. I wish I didn't—and I feel guilty as hell about it—but I can't go back on what I said.'

'Of course you can.' Gina was calm. 'We love each other.'

'I *don't* love you. I'm sorry, Gina, but I don't.'

The curve of the rose pink mouth turned downwards. 'Is

it because of something Emily has said to you? She always was a moral little prig!'

'Emily has nothing to do with it. At least she ... I mean I——'

'You love her,' Gina interrupted harshly. 'You've fallen for my stand-in!' She gave a shrill laugh. 'It would be funny if it weren't so pathetic. Brilliant Luke Adams falling for a nobody! And why? Because he doesn't need *me* any more! Because he used me to get to the top and now he thinks he can stay there all by himself!'

'Don't talk like that. You know it isn't true.'

'Of course it's true. All your talk about guilt! You aren't capable of feeling guilty. You're a ruthless power-seeker. You only wanted me because I was Charles's wife; because I could put in a good word for you!'

'No!' Luke protested. 'Don't minimise what we had together. I did love you. If we had married—or if you had come away with me in the beginning—things might have worked out differently.'

'You never loved me,' Gina reiterated. 'I was just one step on the Harrick ladder to the chairmanship!'

'My love for you had nothing to do with my career,' he said firmly. 'I was willing to give up the City and go back to university if you'd come to live with me.'

'You knew I'd never do that. Do you think I'd have been happy to live on a don's salary in a university backwater!'

Gina was almost sobbing with rage and her mascara made dark streaks down her cheeks. Yet she still looked lovely and Luke was moved by her tears. 'Don't let's say bitter things to each other, Gina. It won't change the position and it's a pity to spoil what we had. You are a beautiful woman and you should marry someone who loves you.'

'*You* love me,' she cried, her tears falling faster.

'I don't.'

'Then it *is* Emily, isn't it?' The blue eyes darkened at Luke's nod. 'You're mad!' she sobbed. 'She'll never be able to give you what I can. She's a child, Luke, and I'm a woman.'

'A beautiful woman,' he repeated, 'and one with whom I've been very happy. But what we felt for each other wasn't love. It was intrigue and excitement. It wouldn't have lasted in the mundane atmosphere of daily living.'

'You've worked it all out, haven't you?' she said scornfully. 'Trust an academic to analyse away his guilt!'

'I'll never be able to do that. I'll always feel guilty for what happened. But what I said to you just now, I believe. Our love wouldn't have lasted in a marriage.'

He crossed to the door, but she ran forward and barred the way. 'Where are you going?'

'To my club.'

'You promised to have dinner with me.'

'There's no point in my staying. If I do we'll quarrel.' He disengaged his arm. 'I'm sorry if I've hurt you, but there was no other way. It would have been impossible to live a lie.'

'You've never lived anything *but* a lie,' she said bitterly.

Helplessly Luke stared at her, not knowing how to combat her anger or how to lessen her hurt. 'I would have given ten years of my life not to have come here tonight and told you this. I can't change facts.'

'So you're going to change women instead!' she shrilled. 'And what will you say to Emily when somebody else takes *her* place? You'd better be careful about it, Luke, she won't be as easy to get rid of as me. You're married to *her*!'

Silently he turned on his heel and strode into the hall. Gina called his name and he turned and looked at her. She was in complete control of herself once more; all anger gone, her face and voice serene.

'Charles has left me all his shares in the company, Luke. If you walk out on me, I will do everything in my power to have you removed from the Board.'

A feeling of relief—strong as a tidal wave—washed over him. He had longed for a way to expiate his guilt and unbelievably Gina had given it to him.

'You won't need to try very hard, Gina. I'll resign from Harricks in the morning.'

Dumbfounded, she glared at him. 'I suppose you've had a better offer from Wilson?'

'No offer at all.'

'You're lying! He's been trying to get you for more than a year. Well, I won't let you go. I'll hold you to your contract!'

'I have no contract with Harricks,' Luke replied. 'But even if I did, nothing would make me stick to it. I intend to work for a company where I know that what I achieve won't depend on the chairman's wife!' Opening the front door, he slammed it behind him and ran down the steps to his car.

Only as he sat at the wheel and saw his hands tremble did he realise how much the scene had taken out of him. Slowly he drove round the block and parked, waiting for a few moments until the sledgehammer which seemed to be pounding in his head, had eased. Only then did he re-start the car and drive towards his club and the comfort of male society, where no questions would be asked and no statement expected. A snack and a couple of aspirins should see him all right in an hour. Then he would go home and tell Emily he loved her. That was something he should have done the moment he had discovered it.

What did it matter if she did not love him in return? He was prepared to spend the rest of his life trying to make her change her mind. He did not care on what terms she stayed with him, so long as she stayed. He sighed heavily. He even loved her enough to give her her freedom if that was what she really wanted. But he dared not think of that at this stage. Time enough to do so if all else failed.

CHAPTER THIRTEEN

EMILY glanced at her wrist watch and wondered if it had stopped. Could it only be eight-thirty? It seemed as if the evening had dragged on for hours. Yet the ticking was steady and she knew it was her own misery that was making the time drag. What was Luke doing now? Not for a moment had she believed his story that he was working late. He was with Gina. There was no doubt of it.

She jumped to her feet and walked restlessly round the room. Far below she could hear the hum of traffic and see the lights of cars moving through the darkness of the park. As always the view held her enthralled. She knew how much she would miss it when she returned to the country, knew too that she would miss so much more than just the view. These past months with Luke had served to show her how irrevocable her love for him was; a love that not even her scorn of him could destroy. Seeing Roger today had made this more clear than ever. She would never be able to marry anyone else.

She twisted the diamond wedding ring on her finger, and the jewels glittered through her tears. What an empty band it was, signifying nothing. If only she could turn back the clock to the time when she had never known Luke; when she had been heart-free and full of hope for the future, instead of having no heart to give to anyone else and no future to consider.

Voices in the hall roused her from her reverie, and wondering who could be calling at this late hour she opened the door. Her hands clenched as she saw Gina.

'I'll keep my coat,' Gina was saying to the butler. 'I won't be staying long.' Bright blue eyes flashed in Emily's direction. 'I took a chance on finding you in.'

'Luke isn't here.' Emily was annoyed to find her voice shaking.

'I know that, darling. I've just seen him at my house.'

Automatically Emily glanced at the front door and Gina interpreted the look and smiled. 'He's gone to his club. You know what cowards men are. They always rush away and leave their women to do their dirty work for them.'

As she spoke she walked past Emily into the drawing-room and perched on the arm of the settee, dropping her mink coat from around her. To Emily's anguished eyes she looked more enchanting than ever, thinner since Charles's death, yet incredibly beautiful. No wonder Luke loved her.

'What do you want to see me about, Gina?' she asked quickly. 'You've obviously come here to say something.'

'I'm not sure where to begin,' Gina confessed. 'It seemed so easy when I was driving here, but now we're face to face.' The blue eyes were pleading. 'Emily dear, I've al-ways been so fond of you that I——'

'Say what you've come to say,' Emily interrupted, 'and cut the pretence.'

Gina's head lowered and she surveyed one of her slender feet as if seeking inspiration there. 'Luke and I want to get married as soon as possible. He has changed his mind about our waiting. That's why he came to see me tonight. And that's why I'm here now.' She looked up. 'He didn't want to tell you himself because he feels guilty at the way he insisted on your staying with him for another six months.'

'He has no need to feel guilty.' With difficulty Emily managed to get out the words. 'I offered to go last night, but he wouldn't let me.'

The blue eyes glinted. 'That shows you how guilty he feels! He's afraid he's spoiled your life.'

'He's done a good job of spoiling his own!'

'What is that supposed to mean?'

Emily shrugged. 'Forget it. I was being too personal. It's none of my business what you and he do. But I'll pack and leave tomorrow.' Gina's glance at her wrist watch was too pointed for her to misunderstand its meaning. 'You aren't expecting me to leave tonight, are you?'

'The idea did cross my mind,' Gina admitted. 'As I said,

Luke is so embarrassed about it all that I think he was hoping to find you had gone by the time he came back.'

Fury at being so ignominiously turned out of her own home—for in recent months she had come to regard it as such—almost made Emily lose her temper. But determination not to let Gina know how hurt she was, acted as a brake, easing her anger until it had abated sufficiently for her to control it.

'I've aleady told you that Luke has no reason to feel guilty,' she said calmly. 'He knows very well I want to leave; that's why we had a row last night.'

'Luke hasn't been himself since Charles died.' Gina's voice was low. 'It has been a trying time for us both—especially for Luke. He's a virile man, and not being able to see me . . . I suppose it has affected him.'

Emily swallowed hard. She was not an innocent; she knew what Luke's love for Gina meant to him. But to hear it given utterance was more than she could bear.

'I'll leave—I'll leave tonight,' she jerked out.

'I knew you would be sensible.' Gina's voice was a purr. 'I told Luke he had nothing to worry about.' With a waft of perfume far more subtle than her conversation had been, she left the flat.

For a long moment Emily stood in the drawing-room willing herself not to break down. She must pack and leave quickly, while she still had the strength to do so.

Moving like an automaton, she went to her room. Her cases were stacked in the back of a cupboard—luckily she had forgotten to ask the chauffeur to take them down to the storeroom which each apartment was allocated in the basement—and she pulled them out and began to toss her things into them, uncaring whether or not they creased. In the country she would have no need for glamorous clothes; besides, she could never bear to wear them again, knowing with what high hopes of making Luke love her she had bought them.

She was packing the last of her cases when she heard an exclamation behind her and, swinging round, saw Luke by the door. She was vividly reminded of the last time she had been packing to leave; though tonight there was a different look on Luke's face, a different urgency in his voice as he strode into the room and demanded to know what she was doing.

'What do you think I'm doing?' she said. 'I'm leaving you—as you've requested.'

'You're *not* leaving me!' He lunged forward and slammed the case shut, nearly trapping her fingers.

Again he was repeating a gesture he had made before, and she was struck by the ridiculousness of the situation. If it were not such a tragedy for her she could almost look on it as a black comedy.

'What's the matter with you, Luke? One minute you ask me to go and then you act like a maniac when I do.'

'I don't know what you're talking about,' he said harshly. 'I've never asked you to go.'

'Gina did it for you!'

His head tilted sharply. 'What's Gina got to do with it?'

'Everything.' Emily re-opened the lid of her case and continued her packing. Her hands shook so much that the dress she was folding fell on to the bed. Afraid that if she tried to refold it she would give away her agitation, she went to the dressing-table and pretended to rummage in the drawers.

'What has Gina got to do with your going?' he repeated, and was suddenly behind her, his fingers digging into the flesh of her arms as he spun her round to face him.

'You ask a thing like that?' she flared. 'You told her to come here. You wanted to save yourself the embarrassment of admitting you'd made a mistake in wanting me to stay on. Well, if it's any consolation to you, I made a mistake too. I should have left you the day Charles died.'

'No,' Luke grated. 'I wanted you to stay then and I want you to stay now.'

'Are you planning to start a harem?'

'I'm planning to start a marriage,' he said. 'With *you.*'

He bent to pull her closer, but she beat her fists against his chest. 'You're out of your mind,' she cried, and tried to pull free of him. 'Let me go!'

'Never! You're mine and I'm not letting you go anywhere! I've been at my club for the past two hours figuring a way to tell you how I feel, and I still don't know how to begin. I love you, Emily. I can't let you walk out of my life.'

Her breath caught in her throat and she expelled it slowly, afraid that if she breathed out too fast it would dispel the words. 'You love me?' she whispered.

'More than life itself. If you leave me, I'm finished.'

'But I ... No, it isn't true. You've never said ... never given a sign ... No.'

'Yes,' he repeated. 'I love you. I was afraid to tell you before in case you took fright and ran away—the way you're running now.'

'I'm not running away.' As she remembered Gina, Emily's voice grew hard. 'You asked me to go and I'm going.'

'Gina asked you,' he corrected. 'I had no idea she would dare to come here and ...' His fingers were like steel on her flesh. 'I love you, Emily. I think I fell in love with you when we were in Paris, but I was too blind to see it. It wasn't until a couple of months ago that I knew for certain.'

She still found it hard to accept what he said. 'You love Gina. You can't have changed your mind so quickly.'

'It wasn't quick. I fought against it. I couldn't believe such a thing was happening to me. But it was no use. You were constantly in my mind. Everything you did—said— the way you looked.' His voice was fast, the words blurred and unmonitored. 'Being with Gina was a torment. Whenever she came near me I saw *your* face; heard *your* voice. I thought I was going out of my mind.'

'Perhaps you were,' she said sarcastically, her emotions still raw from the pounding Gina had given them. 'I'm not your type, Luke. I'm no chocolate box beauty, nor am I rich and well-connected.'

'Stop it!' He caught her arm and shook her. 'Say what

184

you like about *me,* but don't denigrate yourself! You're beautiful in a way Gina can never be, and you're rich in compassion and warmth—even though you're not showing much warmth to *me.*'

'Do you expect me to?'

'No, I don't. But however much you despise me, it's no more than I despise myself.' He stepped away from her, his mobile mouth lifting in a bitter smile. 'At least you and Gina have one thing in common. You both hate me!'

She ignored the comment. 'Gina said you wanted me to go away. That you begged her to come and tell me to leave at once.'

His eyes blazed, their pale grey so intensified that they gave the impression of clashing steel. 'It was the exact opposite. I saw Gina and told her we were through. She took it badly and——'

'I'm not surprised,' Emily cut in. 'You loved her for two years. You only married *me* so that you could go on seeing her. You can't blame her for being hurt.'

'I blame no one except myself.' He put his hand to his temple as if there was a sudden pain there. 'I tried to deny what I felt for you, but I couldn't. You made my feelings for Gina seem tawdry.'

Emily bit back a sigh. Tawdry. It was the right word to describe his shabby and deceitful love affair. Yet she still could not forget that it had filled his life for so long. An image of him holding Gina flashed into her mind, and an agony of jealousy made her want to hurt him. 'You're not the faithful type, are you, Luke? What confidence can I have in a future with you?'

'Did Gina say that to you?' he said bitterly. 'Will I have to spend the rest of my life paying for a mistake? I'm a man, Emily, not a plaster saint! Many men fall in love with the wrong woman, but that doesn't mean they can't fall in love with the right one! I'm not making excuses,' he went on in a cracked voice. 'Merely trying to make you see I'm not quite the blackguard you think. If you want to go ahead and leave me, I can't stop you. But at least let me go on seeing you. Perhaps in time I can make you change your mind about me. I don't care how long I have to wait.'

Emily tried to subdue the wild elation bubbling inside her. 'Time won't make any difference to the way I feel.'

'I see.' His lower lips trembled as if he could not control it, and she moved back in order to stare into his face. His eyes were intent on hers, and as she stared into them she saw that they were shimmering with tears. Horrified, she gave a murmur.

'Luke, don't! I can't bear to see you cry.'

'Forgive me.' He turned his back on her and walked to the door. 'Will you at least let me take you down to the cottage?'

'I would prefer you to take me to Paris,' she whispered shakily. 'We never did have a proper honeymoon there!'

Slowly he turned, as if he did not believe he had heard correctly. Then the look on her face sent him striding to her side. Wordlessly he pulled her close and she felt the warmth of his body and the tears on his cheeks as he rested his face upon hers.

'Do you mean it?' he said hoarsely. 'Last night you said you loved Roger. Now you say . . . You're not just sorry for me?'

'I'm sorry for *me*,' she said crossly. 'When I think of the time we've wasted I could——'

'Oh, Emily!' He gave a shout of laughter. 'Was there ever a girl like you!'

'There'd better not be. I'm no Gina. I'll never let you go. Not even if you change your mind a hundred times!' She clung to him. 'I'm shameless, aren't I?'

'I hope so,' he said thickly. 'It augurs well for our honeymoon if you are!'

Her laugh was tremulous, dying quickly as his mouth covered hers. There was no gentleness in his touch—he was too overwrought for that—only a deep and passionate longing that awakened an equal longing in her. His hands moved across her back and down her spine, pressing her body along the length of his so that it was easy to feel his

186

urgent need of her.

'I love you so much,' he said. 'Without you I'm nothing.' His hands cupped her breasts. 'I'll phone the office in the morning and tell them I'll be away for a week. I can't make it any longer, my darling, but once I've resigned from Harricks we'll take a proper honeymoon. Six months if you like, lotus-eating on some tropical island.'

'I don't care where I am, as long as I'm with you.' She stroked the back of his neck. 'You don't need to resign from Harrick's because of me. I'm not jealous of Gina any more. Only sorry for her.'

'I'm not. When I think of how nearly she came to parting us ...' He lowered his head and ran his lips along the curve of her cheek to her throat. 'My love ... I'll spend the rest of my life showing you how much I want you.'

'Begin now,' she commanded, twining her fingers through his thick, silver-blond hair.

'Don't you want to wait till we get to Paris?' he teased.

'We can begin again in Paris!'

'And again and again and again,' he said upon her mouth. 'But for the first time ...'

With their arms around each other there was no more need for words.

Doctor Nurse Romances

and March's
stories of romantic relationships behind the scenes
of modern medical life are:

SISTER IN CHARGE
by Judith Worthy

When Nurse Dilys Davies decides to run the nursing
home left to her in her grandmother's will she does not
expect to find the raging village feud or the unpleasant-
ness of the handsome local doctor ...

MARRY ME, STRANGER
by Anne Vinton.

Sister Laura Bradfield has a very hard time when she
agrees to work with the handsome but unpopular
Doctor Warwick. Things go from bad to worse, but not
before she discovers she is falling in love ...

Mills & Boon
Best Seller Romances

The very best of Mills & Boon Romances
brought back for those of you who missed
them when they were first published.

In April
we bring back the following four
great romantic titles.

DARLING JENNY
by Janet Dailey

Jennifer Glenn, smarting from a disastrous love affair, had
taken herself off to the skiing grounds of Wyoming to 'get
away from it all' and lend a hand to her busy sister Sheila at
the same time. She never expected to fall in love again so soon,
and certainly not with the man who was himself in love with
Sheila!

THE WARM WIND OF FARIK
by Rebecca Stratton

Linsie Palmer was a very new journalist on her very first assign-
ment. The disturbing Celik Demaril was the man she had to
interview. When he refused to see her Linsie decided to stow
away on his yacht — with disastrous consequences!

THE MAN AT KAMBALA
by Kay Thorpe

Sara lived with her father at Kambala in Kenya and was
accustomed to do as she pleased there. She certainly didn't
think much of Steve York, the impossible man who came to
take charge in her father's absence. 'It's asking for trouble to
run around a game reserve as if it were a play park,' he told
her. Was Sara right to ignore him?

FOOD FOR LOVE
by Rachel Lindsay

Amanda could see problems ahead when her boss, Clive Brand,
began taking serious interest in her, so she changed her job.
And found still more problems in the person of that mysterious,
maddening man, Red Clark!

Choose from this selection of

Mills & Boon
FAVOURITES
— ALL HIGHLY RECOMMENDED

ORDER NOW FOR DIRECT DELIVERY

☐ C271
NO QUARTER ASKED
Janet Dailey

☐ C272
THE LIBRARY TREE
Lilian Peake

☐ C273
MIRANDA'S MARRIAGE
Margery Hilton

☐ C274
PALACE OF THE
POMEGRANATE
Violet Winspear

☐ C275
SAVAGE LAND
Janet Dailey

☐ C276
DARK MOONLESS
NIGHT
Anne Mather

☐ C277
PARISIAN ADVENTURE
Elizabeth Ashton

☐ C278
THE TOWER OF THE
CAPTIVE
Violet Winspear

☐ C279
THE BEADS OF
NEMESIS
Elizabeth Hunter

☐ C280
HEART OF THE LION
Roberta Leigh

☐ C281
THE IRON MAN
Kay Thorpe

☐ C282
THE RAINBOW BIRD
Margaret Way

ONLY **65p** EACH

SIMPLY TICK ✓ YOUR SELECTION(S)
ABOVE, THEN JUST COMPLETE AND
POST THE ORDER FORM OVERLEAF